ANIMAL HEROES

27 True Stories

Some of the material in this book was previously published as
Animal Heroes and *More Animal Heroes*.

KARLEEN BRADFORD

SCHOLASTIC CANADA LTD.

Scholastic Canada Ltd.
175 Hillmount Road, Markham, Ontario, Canada L6C 1Z7

Scholastic Inc.
555 Broadway, New York, NY 10012, USA

Scholastic Australia Pty Limited
PO Box 579, Gosford, NSW 2250, Australia

Scholastic New Zealand Ltd.
Private Bag 94407, Greenmount, Auckland, New Zealand

Scholastic Publications Ltd.
Villiers House, Clarendon Avenue, Leamington Spa
Warwickshire CV32 5PR, UK

COVER PHOTO CREDIT:
KD6470 © 2000 Mallaun/Mauritius/H. Armstrong Roberts

Canadian Cataloguing in Publication Data
Bradford, Karleen
Animal heroes : 27 true stories

ISBN 0-439-98830-6

1. Animal heroes – Juvenile literature. I. Title.
SF416.2.B73 2001   j636   C00-932573-5

6 5 4 3 2   Printed in Canada   1 2 3 4 5 / 0

For Casey
and Kitty Kat

Contents

Ralston Purina Hall of Fame
inductees included in this book are:

Balloo and Jessie

Cali

Euchre

Grizzly

Lindy

Nago

Shana

Topnotch

Bruno

Charlie

Ewo

Hustler

Nellie

Sam

Tia

Wrinkles

Acknowledgements

I would like to thank the owners of these brave animals for sharing their stories.

As well, I would like to thank Sid Horton, George Hickinbottom, and Jim Allaway, editor of the *Navy News* in Portsmouth, England, for the information and anecdotes they sent to me about Simon, the Ship's Cat. George also supplied me with information about Ricky, the pet who went to war.

Thank you to Julia McKinnell, producer of CBC's *Basic Black*, who put me in touch with Philip Gonzalez, the owner of the incredible Ginny. Mike Mackintosh, Head of Wildlife Services for the City of Vancouver, and Graham C. Ford, Assistant Manager of the Stanley Park Zoological Gardens, were very helpful with the story of Tuk, the polar bear, whom I was lucky enough to meet personally — although not too personally. Bill and Jane Thornton, of Canadian Guide Dogs for the Blind, in Manotick, Ontario, were also extremely helpful.

My morning dog-walking friend, Tom Corat, owner of two Great (in every sense of the word) Bouviers, put me onto the story of Max. My good friend Marilyn Lister, a Bernese Mountain dog owner and enthusiast, found the account of Balloo and Jessie for me. Katherine Paterson, another friend who went on the animal hero alert for me, and who has written about search-and-rescue dogs herself, told me about Jiggs.

I have Tony German, of Old Chelsea, Quebec, to thank for the story of the rabbit, and for background information from his book, *The Sea Is At Our Gates: The History of the Canadian Navy* (McClelland & Stewart, 1990).

Finally, I would like to thank Ralston Purina Canada, Inc., for their assistance.

Karleen Bradford

Hustler

HUSTLER

The Dog Who Wouldn't Quit

Debbie Inions went to a dog show and fell in love with a six-month-old black and tan German Shepherd. She asked his owners if he was for sale, but they said no. Two months later they called Debbie to offer her the dog. Although they loved him and thought the world of him, he wasn't working out for them. He was a "very relaxed kind of dog," and just didn't do well in the competitive atmosphere of the show ring. Since he'd been brought up in a house with children and was "a real spoiled couch potato," Debbie was sure that he would make a good pet for her children. She brought the pup home to their farm, and named him Hustler.

The Inions have a herd of cattle, and Debbie decided to see if she could also make a working dog out of Hustler. He had never even seen a cow before, but he seemed to know what to do. Calving was starting, and they were getting the heifers into the barn. Hustler jumped right in, nipping at their heels and moving them along. Within a short while he was working with Debbie and her husband, Brian, getting cattle into the chute, loading them, cutting out cows that needed help — anything that had to be done, he could do it. "It was like having two extra guys around to help," Debbie says.

She also says he's "quite the character." When he's working cattle, Hustler can be as aggressive as he needs to be to get the job done. At other times, Hustler strolls right through the herd without causing any problems at all. Sometimes he even sleeps with the cows. Debbie says, "He's got two different sides to him. He knows when he's on duty and when he's off. He's a real sweetheart."

It's true. His previous owner kept birds — cockatiels and little budgies — and let them fly loose in her house. Hustler once found one downstairs and carried it gently upstairs between his teeth to lay it at her feet, completely unharmed. He even helped her retrieve some baby birds that had fallen out of a nest — he found one on the ground and carried it back to her.

Hustler did have to learn about horses, though. One of them in particular didn't appreciate dogs running too close to his heels. It took a few minor kicks, and then one bad one that required surgery to an eye, for Hustler to get the message. Hustler still happily runs with horses — at a respectful distance.

One evening, after she had settled Tracy and Curtis down for the night, Debbie decided to make a last check on the cattle. Brian was out seeding barley in one of the fields, and she knew he would be working late to get it all done that night. She figured she would be gone for half an hour at most. She mounted her quarter horse and, together with Hustler, headed into the bush toward the field where the cattle were.

As they were going up a hill, a sudden noise at the top caused Debbie's horse to shy. He jumped sideways, down the hill. Debbie, a good horse-woman, managed to stay on; but then, because there was a fence in front of the spooked horse and he couldn't run straight out, he spun around. There was a brush pile there, and he jumped again. This time Debbie was thrown.

"I landed on my leg," Debbie says. "Before the rest of me even hit the ground, I knew it was broken." (In fact, two bones had been broken in three places.)

Debbie lay dazed, the pain from her leg almost overwhelming her. The horse, calm now, ambled over and sniffed at her, perhaps curious about why she wasn't getting back on. Debbie realized that she was not going to be able to move. She'd taken a shortcut through the bush and knew there was no chance of anyone happening upon her there. She thought if she could send her horse home and someone saw him they might come looking for her.

> **"He's got two different sides to him. He knows when he's on duty and when he's off. He's a real sweetheart."**

"I threw sticks at him and stuff, and kind of

chased him away. He went, but he went back the way we had come, which was through bushes and behind the barn where he couldn't be seen by anybody. I knew that wasn't going to be much help."

All the while, Hustler stayed by her side. Then suddenly he went charging off through the bush. Debbie thought, Well, that's just fine. Here I am with a broken leg and he's off chasing some deer.

"I never thought anything more about it, but then he was back, standing over me, and he was snarling. All I could see were his teeth, and he looked so vicious! I'd never seen him look like that, because he's not a vicious dog. I looked over my shoulder, in the the direction he was looking, and there were two coyotes snarling back at him."

The coyotes were only about four metres away, and inching closer. Hustler jumped over Debbie and attacked. They ran off into the bushes, and he followed. Debbie watched them disappear.

"I didn't know who was going to come back, Hustler or the coyotes," she says.

Finally Hustler did return, but so did the coyotes. Evening darkened into night. Every time Hustler chased the coyotes away, they came stubbornly back. Debbie's leg was bleeding heavily; the scent of the blood must have been irresistible to them.

"It got quite scary," Debbie says now. "Each time I just wondered how much longer he was going to be able to keep those coyotes off me, and when was it going to be the coyotes that came back through the bush instead of him?"

But Hustler came back every time. Debbie got

weaker, and started shaking with shock and cold. She wrapped her arms around Hustler and pressed herself as close as she could to the warmth of his body. The coyotes didn't give up. They came back again and again. Again and again, Hustler tore himself away to go after them. The black night was filled with their howling.

Brian Inions got home about one-thirty in the morning. He was tired, but the barley crop was all planted. The house was quiet; he figured Debbie and the children were asleep. He started to get himself something to eat. Then he realized that Debbie's boots were gone. He looked out and saw that her horse was gone, too. He went in to Tracy, woke her, and asked if she knew where Debbie was. Tracy murmured that her mother had gone out to check the cows. Only half awake, she didn't realize what the time was.

> **"I looked over my shoulder, in the the direction he was looking, and there were two coyotes snarling back at him."**

Brian jumped on their all-terrain vehicle and roared out to look for Debbie. There was a lot of land to cover, however. A lot of hills and bush. After two hours of fruitless searching, he still hadn't found her. Then he saw Hustler break into a clearing in hot pursuit of two coyotes, and he knew Debbie couldn't be far away.

"I hardly had any voice by that time, I was so weak," Debbie says. "I'd been yelling at the coyotes, and Hustler had been barking at them. In between chasing them he'd come and sit over me just like he was guarding me."

By following Hustler, Brian finally found Debbie. He realized that she was in too much pain for him to try to move her or take her back on the all-terrain vehicle. He would have to go back alone and telephone for an ambulance.

"I suddenly panicked when he left, thinking that Hustler might go back after him," Debbie says. "Then I'd be left alone with those coyotes. It was pitch dark and starting to spit rain. The wind had come up, and I was really cold. Then I looked up and there was Hustler, sitting right by me, just like he had been all the night."

Brian was back as soon as possible with blankets. He wrapped Debbie up in them, and together they waited. The ambulance managed to make it down the trail, arriving soon after. But even while they were loading Debbie into it, even with all the people there, the coyotes still circled, relentless and stubborn.

> **"I didn't know who was going to come back, Hustler or the coyotes."**

Debbie was in the hospital for two weeks. During all that time, Hustler worried. Every time Brian came home, the dog would run out hopefully to greet the truck, only to be disappointed when Debbie wasn't in it. When Debbie finally did come home, the first thing he did was sniff her injured leg from hip to ankle, almost as if to make certain she was all right.

Cali

CALI

The Guard Cat

There was a cage full of kittens at the Toronto Humane Society animal shelter when Lauren MacLaren went to pick out a pet. They had been found abused and tossed away in a bag. Four of them were males: black, white or orange. They were tumbling around and wrestling with each other. As soon as they spotted Lauren, they clambered over each other excitedly in their efforts to get her attention. But Lauren was looking at their tiny, frightened, calico-patterned sister, huddled away in a corner at the back. Lauren knew this was the kitten she'd come to find.

She brought Cali home with her, and during the next six years they became the best of friends. "She's my shadow," Lauren says. "Everywhere I go, she goes."

One night Lauren was sleeping in her ground floor bedroom. It was almost two o'clock in the morning. Suddenly Cali leaped up onto the bed and pounced on Lauren. Lauren woke with a start. Confused and half asleep, she couldn't imagine what was the matter with her cat. Cali pawed at her, crying, then started a low, rumbling kind of growl. She wouldn't leave Lauren alone.

Finally, Lauren sat up, thoroughly awake. At that moment she heard a crunching noise outside the bedroom door, which opened onto the deck outside. It was footsteps, coming stealthily up the driveway! She heard them come up onto the deck. She heard them come closer. Then, to her horror, she saw the doorknob begin to turn.

The door was locked, but as the knob rattled, Lauren panicked. The house she lived in was old. Just how strong was the wooden door?

There was a telephone beside the bed, but the window beside the door was open a crack. Lauren was afraid that if she used the bedroom phone the intruder outside her door would hear. Carefully, she slipped out of bed and crawled into the kitchen. As soon as Cali realized that her friend was aware of the danger and was doing something about it, she did the only thing a sensible cat would do. She hid under the bed.

> **"She knew those footsteps weren't normal for that time of night, and she knew she had to wake me up."**

As quietly as she could, Lauren phoned 9-1-1.

"The people on 9-1-1 were wonderful," Lauren says now. "They calmed me right down. I was terrified. Your imagination does go a little crazy in a situation like that. But they kept me on the phone and they told me not to worry — I might not see the police, but they had been called and were already there."

And they were. Within minutes the intruder was captured, right on Lauren's back deck, and placed under arrest. And Cali watched it all — from under the bed's dust ruffle.

Cali received the Ralston Purina Animal Hall of Fame Award for her quick intelligence and for the alertness that saved Lauren from an intruder that night. Cali took her place proudly at the ceremony, right by Hustler, the German Shepherd, and Tia, the chocolate Lab, who were also being honoured that year.

"She looked so small up there, beside those two big dogs," Lauren says. "And they'd done such brave things to save their masters — fight off coyotes and pull a boat to shore . . ." Lauren laughs, but her voice is full of pride. "Maybe cats can't do the things dogs can do, but they are very aware. The instinct is there. She knew those footsteps weren't normal for that time of night, and she knew she had to wake me up. Mind you," she adds, "once she knew I was awake, that was it. I mean, she wasn't going to stand around and bare her teeth at anybody!"

Besides the medal and several other prizes, Cali won a year's supply of cat food. To express her thanks for her friend, Lauren donated it all to the animal shelter that brought them together.

Ginny

GINNY

A Cat's Best Friend

Philip Gonzalez had suffered an industrial accident that left him partially disabled, and he was depressed.

"You need a dog," his friend told him, so they went to the animal shelter near Philip's home in Long Beach, New York. The man at the shelter worried that perhaps Philip wouldn't be able to take care of a dog, so he suggested a cat.

"I don't want a cat," Philip answered. "I want a dog. A big dog."

The shelter officer showed him the dogs they had there, but none seemed right to Philip.

"I've got a couple more in the back," the man said, so they went to have a look.

The first dog Philip saw was a female Doberman Pinscher.

"I don't want a female," he said.

Then he saw a young Schnauzer/Husky mix. When the dog saw Philip, she got up, came over to him and started licking his hand.

13

"That's a first," the shelter officer said. "We haven't been able to get this dog to respond to us at all."

"I'll take him," Philip said.

"It's a her," was the answer.

"Well, then, I don't want her. Besides, she's too small."

"Take her around the block," the officer insisted. Philip's friend urged the same. So Philip gave in. Halfway around the block, he looked down at the dog following him. She looked back up at him, and that was it. Ginny was his. He took her back to the shelter and told them he was taking the dog.

On the way out, Ginny stopped at one

> **"She looked back at me, and I knew she was asking me to get that kitten for her, so I said, 'Okay, Ginny, I'll take the cat.'"**

of the cages and sniffed at it. There was a black puppy in it. Ginny started to lick the puppy. "That's her pup," the officer explained. "She's only about a year old, but she had three puppies when we found her abandoned in the closet of an empty house. The others have found homes — I'm sure this one will, too." And it did.

But Ginny's maternal instinct just grew stronger. The first day Philip took her for a walk where he lived, they came across a cat. Ginny pulled on her leash, and Philip, still not too strong after his accident, dropped it. She ran toward the cat, and he was afraid she was going to attack. Far from it.

"She and that cat starting kissing each other, and then they played for almost an hour," says Philip.

Ginny loved every cat she saw, and soon Philip was feeding the strays around his house. He took Ginny back to the animal shelter for a visit, and she headed straight for the cat cages. She put her paws up on one and started whimpering.

"She looked back at me, and I knew she was asking me to get that kitten for her, so I said, 'Okay, Ginny, I'll take the cat,'" Philip says. "I figured she liked playing with the stray cats so much, she wanted one of her own."

Philip brought the little white kitten home and named her Madam. About two days later, he found out she couldn't hear a thing, but neither he nor Ginny minded that.

On another visit to the shelter a couple of weeks later, Ginny picked out another cat: Revlon, who had only one eye. Then Philip took Ginny to the veterinarian's for a checkup. There, she spotted a cat that the vet was going to put down. It had no hind feet, and it was very wild. Ginny made it clear that she wanted it.

"Ginny, this cat's wild," Philip told her, but she wouldn't listen. So Betty Boop went home with Philip and Ginny, and she got on just fine.

The next two months brought two more cats, Topsy and Vogue. On a walk, Ginny got off the leash again and ran into an abandoned building. She came out carrying a kitten in her mouth. It seemed hurt, so

Philip took it to the vet, who found that it was brain-damaged.

"You want me to put it down, right?" the vet asked.

Philip looked at Ginny, who was watching them anxiously.

"No," he answered, "I don't think Ginny would like that."

So Topsy joined the growing family.

Ginny rescued Vogue from some people who were kicking her in the street. At first, Philip thought the tiny creature was a kitten too, like Topsy, but the vet said she was eight or ten years old.

"People around here can be mean to cats and throw rocks at them. They're really leery of humans, but every cat in the neighbourhood trusts Ginny."

Once she started eating, she grew into a very big cat.

One rescue followed another, and before long, Philip had nine cats — quite a number for someone who hadn't wanted even one. But Ginny wasn't through saving cats. Not by a long shot. The place where Philip lives is a resort area. People come for the summer, bringing their cats, and when they go home in the fall, they leave their cats behind. Life is hard for the cats, and they have to fight for survival. Ginny helps whenever she can.

"The cats on the street trust Ginny more than they trust me," Philip says. "People around here can be mean to cats and throw rocks at them. They're really leery of humans, but every cat in the neighbourhood trusts Ginny."

Ginny doesn't put up with human bullies, letting them know with a good growl just what she thinks of them. But she'll protect any cat at all. King Arthur is a big Russian Blue cat, grey with white patches. He was a street bully, but then the other cats got together and ganged up on him. He fled to Ginny, and she protected him. Philip brought him home, and, under Ginny's watchful eye, he behaves beautifully.

Other animals are wary of Ginny, too. One of the cats in Philip's household, Dotty, used to live in a junkyard. "There were a bunch of chickens running loose in the yard that used to beat up Dotty all the time. About eight of them, that used to attack her," remembers Philip. "Ginny went over there and stopped that. Those chickens ran when they saw her. Then she found this really big tiger-striped cat there too, with a hurt leg." Both Dotty and Napoleon, the tiger-stripe, went home with Ginny and Philip.

Because of Ginny, Philip has a reputation for being a cat's best friend as well. One day, someone called Philip and told him they had a female purebred Manx cat named Sheba, but they couldn't keep her. Could he take her? Silly question. Philip picked her up and took her to the vet to have her spayed. There, he found out that Sheba was really a male, so there was a quick name change: Sheba became King Solomon.

These days, Philip feeds about ten cats on his terrace and goes on rounds twice a day to eight different spots, where he and Ginny take care of another sixty to seventy cats. At one of the feeding spots, Ginny ran over to an abandoned car. "She started whimpering and trying to get into it, so I went over," says Philip. "When I got there, I saw this cat lying there, but it had been dead for at least a couple of days. I told Ginny, 'Look, there's nothing I can do. The cat's dead. I'll pick it up later and take it to the shelter.' But she kept whimpering at me and wouldn't leave. I went back, and a kitten put its head up from behind the big cat's body." A closer look revealed another kitten. The two were about two weeks old. It was the first really cold night that winter, and without Ginny's help, the kittens would have been dead by morning. The kittens were very cute, all black with white bibs and feet — "tuxedo kittens," Philip calls them. They were soon adopted.

"Some months go by and she doesn't find a thing, other months, she just keeps on finding cats," Philip says. She's found over two hundred by now. "And I've never had one die," he adds.

Ginny made the front page of their community newspaper, and they did a two-page article on her. She's also had an entire book written about her by Philip himself and Leonore Fleischer. It's called *The Dog Who Rescues Cats: The True Story of Ginny*.

COWS ON GUARD

In August 1996, when Welsh farmer Donald Mottram was knocked off his motorbike and stamped on by an angry 1500-kilogram bull, a large group of his cows came to his rescue. They formed a circle around the badly injured man and kept the bull away. "I have treated the animals reasonably," says Donald, "and they have looked after me in return."

Ewo with Constable MacLean

EWO

Trained to Track

Constable Tom MacLean had never worked with police dogs before, but he'd always had dogs of his own, so he applied for the Canine Team program. He was accepted and assigned a two-and-a-half-year-old, long-haired German Shepherd named Ewo, a dog with "a sort of a wolf look to him." The two began a training course with the Niagara Regional Police Force. Thirteen weeks later, they both graduated with flying colours.

Ewo's specialty is tracking, mostly on a nine-metre lead. Off lead, he is trained to bark when he finds what he is looking for — usually a person — to let Constable MacLean know where he is. Ewo has also learned to jump hurdles and fences, go through tunnels, climb ladders, walk across catwalks, and search for and retrieve objects. He's normally a friendly dog, but is trained to be aggressive when necessary. He will protect Constable MacLean or anybody else, and will chase and apprehend a criminal — by biting and holding the suspect's arm.

Good dogs for the police force are hard to find: only about one in three hundred dogs makes a successful police dog. It might seem surprising that one of the most important things the police look for in a dog is a friendly, sociable nature. This is because, as Constable MacLean says, "you can train a dog to be aggressive, but it's hard to calm a wild one down."

Potential police dogs should have a good retrieval instinct, too. They have to love to chase balls, for example. They can't be afraid of loud noises, traffic, stairs, doorways, slippery floors. They must be confident and brave — but willing to accept their trainer as the boss.

It's a long list of requirements, but Ewo met them all. And training him was easy. "It's harder to train the trainer than the dog, to tell the truth," says Constable MacLean. "Dogs do it naturally."

The key to training a dog is play and a "praise and reward" system. Constable MacLean explains: "When the dog does something good he is rewarded, and we all act goofy and make it fun for him. He remembers, 'Hey, if I do a good job, or do this right, I'm going to get to play.'" The police use a special toy called a Kong, a cone-shaped, bouncy thing that dogs love to chase. The officers hide the Kong, and the dogs learn to track trying to find it. When the Kong is found, the dog gets to play: chasing after the Kong, wrestling with his handler and getting "lots of pats and lots of praise."

All this play makes Ewo great with kids. "Ewo is the kind of dog that you can take into a kindergarten class and the kids can crawl all over him," Constable

MacLean says. The two used to visit classrooms to demonstrate a police dog's skills. Kids loved Ewo's specialty, something no other dog would do.

"We put him in a baby carriage," Constable MacLean remembers. "We put a bonnet on him, and he would just lie there. Then I put on a dress and a wig. We would walk along, and then somebody would steal my purse. Ewo would jump out of the carriage and go and bite the guy. It made a great show."

> "You can train a dog to be aggressive, but it's hard to calm a wild one down."

But for all his playfulness, Ewo was ready in an instant when it was time for him to go to work for real.

On December 17, 1992, an elderly couple returned to their home near Niagara Falls to find three men robbing their house. The men ran out the back door and disappeared into the bushes. The couple called the police.

Constable MacLean and Ewo arrived on the scene about forty minutes later. They knew the direction the men had gone, and Ewo picked up their scent immediately. Constable MacLean put Ewo on his lead. With an escort officer for safety, the team headed into the bush. After a short while, they came across a garbage bag full of Christmas gifts that had been taken from the house. Further on, they found a coat. Ewo was getting excited.

They kept on, across fields, through thick bush, and across dense cornfields. After about an hour, Constable MacLean suddenly saw one of the thieves running ahead of them in the bush. The man stopped and darted behind a tree. As the dog and trainer approached, he suddenly came out from behind the tree, swinging a big stick. Constable MacLean sent Ewo in to attack. Ewo grabbed the man by the arm, and the escort officer arrested him. But that was only the first robber; there were at least two others.

The team kept on tracking for another hour and forty minutes. They crossed a couple of little creeks, and then a big one. There wasn't a lot of snow on the ground, but it was

> **"After he got the first guy, he wanted number two."**

bitterly cold, and this creek was partly frozen. Constable MacLean could tell by the broken ice that one of the men he was pursuing had waded across, and he decided to go after him. He took off his gun-belt and threw it across the creek to an officer on the other side. He threw his gun across, too. Ewo swam across on his lead, then Constable MacLean plunged into the freezing water. Luckily, it wasn't over his head, but it was up to his armpits and the current was strong. With the help of his fellow officer, who pulled on Ewo's lead, Constable MacLean made it across safely. Then he continued tracking, soaking wet and very cold.

Ewo was performing exceptionally well. Normally,

a dog will lose interest after a short period of time — most of the tracks are only a few hundred metres, or at the most a kilometre — but Ewo just went on and on. "After he got the first guy, he wanted number two," the constable remembers. "His interest didn't flag at all."

After about fourteen kilometres, they went into a farmer's field, bordered by bush in which there was an old abandoned car. Ewo went into the bush and started whining and barking, and Constable MacLean found the second thief, dug in under the car. The man was arrested. The third thief got away, but the two who were arrested were confirmed criminals, well known to the police.

Constable MacLean had to go to the hospital to be treated for hypothermia, but didn't have to stay long. As for Ewo, who had worked so hard and for so long in the below-zero weather, he was so tired they had to lift him into the police car.

Ewo is retired now, and Constable MacLean keeps him as a pet, much to his children's delight. During his career, Ewo did many brave things. One of them stands out in the constable's memory — and still brings Ewo rewards.

On Valentine's Day one year, a seventy-two-year-old woman was walking down the street. She was attacked by a young boy, who knocked her down and stole her purse. The elderly woman had a cut in her head, and she had to crawl to a house to get help. Ewo was called and tracked the boy down successfully. The woman's purse was returned to her intact. Every Valentine's Day since then, the grateful woman sends Ewo a big present: a Valentine's card, dog cookies and bones.

"It makes it all worth it," Constable MacLean says.

Ewo was given the Ralston Purina Police Dog of the Year Award in 1994. He took the stage with Constable MacLean, and let everyone know just how pleased he was about it. As the Ralston Purina spokesman was introducing him, Ewo began to talk. He growled and yowled and barked, and went on growling and yowling and barking — so much that the presenter of the award could not make himself heard.

"Do you want to tell the story yourself?" the presenter finally asked.

It seemed very much as if Ewo did.

SCHOOLYARD HERO

In 1999 a 5-year-old rottweiler police dog named Caesar leapt into the path of a bullet, when he tried to disarm a man threatening a schoolyard full of children. Caesar later died of his wounds, but not before his partner Constable Randy Goss and other officers captured the man. Caesar was awarded the Ralston Purina Service Dog of the Year award.

Police Tracking Dogs

Most dogs chosen to be police dogs are not bred especially for this kind of work. Some may be rejects from breeders who know they won't do well in the show ring. Some are dogs who have been training to guide the blind and have proven to be too aggressive for this duty. Some come from owners who couldn't handle them. Many are found through newspaper ads.

Police dog handlers want a dog that is excited and eager to retrieve objects, that is physically and mentally strong, and that isn't gun shy. They look for a dog that isn't scared of people. In a staring match, they want the dog to stare the officer down! Several breeds are good at sniffing out bombs or drugs, but German Shepherds do most of the tracking. They are strong, able to work in hot or cold temperatures, and seem to have the best temperament for the job: usually aggressive, but not overly ferocious.

After undergoing a thorough health examination, each dog is carefully matched up with a police officer, to make a K-9 team. Together, dog and handler go through an intense, fourteen-week course, starting with basic obedience training. The dog is trained to climb ladders and stairs and scale walls as high as seven feet. It must be able to jump through windows, climb barrels, balance and walk on a thin beam and jump more than three metres forward from a standing position. Then the dog is trained in tracking and sniffing.

The dogs are also trained to protect their handlers. If the police officer is struck by a suspect, the K-9 partner will attack without hesitation. Many officers owe their lives to their dogs.

The dog lives with his handler in an outside kennel at the handler's home. The K-9 officer drives a special vehicle to transport his or her dog, and the team must be prepared to respond to a call anytime, day or night. But, although the bond that forms between officer and dog is a strong one, it is a working relationship — the dog is not a pet. And every six weeks, the K-9 team returns for refresher courses to keep up their skills.

Euchre with Senior Constable Killens

EUCHRE

Dog With a Duty

Senior Constable Don Killens of the Ontario Provincial Police got Euchre (pronounced Yooker) when the dog was a year and a half old. Euchre had belonged to an elderly couple who decided that the cute little pup they had brought home had just become too much for them.

The large, dark German Shepherd passed all initial tests and his training with flying colours. He was no longer a pet, but a career dog. And what a career! During his working life, Euchre assisted in tracking down and capturing criminals and found or helped to find many people lost in the area around Perth, Ontario, where Senior Constable Killens is based.

There are plenty of stories about Euchre. Criminals may not have been too pleased with Euchre's successful tracking abilities, but many others, such as Bill Beattie, have reason to be grateful. Bill was on a photography expedition to the east end of Algonquin Park when he fell down a cliff. He was trapped on the cliffside. Four days later, thirsty and tired, he had just about reached the end of his endurance. It was then that a large, dark-coloured dog bounded over to him, licked his face and lay down beside him. Euchre had picked up his scent — off the wind.

Euchre's work was often hazardous, tracking armed and dangerous people. But he had one important advantage.

"Dogs track silently, and we are often in so fast we surprise the bad guys," says Constable Killens. He adds with a smile, "Then I just say to them: 'You've been Euchred!'" (Euchre is a card game. "You've been euchred!" is a phrase used by the winning team.)

Once Euchre found more than a bad guy. He and Constable Killens were tracking a criminal who had robbed a house, when suddenly Euchre veered from the trail and started nosing something. Constable Killens looked down and saw a week-old pup lying whimpering on the ground. He scooped it up and carried it along. Soon after, Euchre managed to track the thief down, and he was arrested. In his pocket was another week-old pup. The OPP officers were able to connect the pups to the robbery, and both were returned unharmed to their mother.

The gentle, patient side of Euchre's nature was put to work as well. Constable Killens often took him to schools for demonstrations, and he went along to Toronto's Hospital for Sick Children when all sixteen OPP dog handlers presented a donation to the hospital.

"He would talk," Constable Killens says. "I would tell him to say goodbye to a classroom of kids and he would bark. I took him into classes often and he thought that was great. I would show them the basic program, then have him go over jumps and climb things. Then I'd take the kids outside and pick a student and show how Euchre could track them. You have to give your dog a lot of praise," he added. "Euchre would roll over to have his belly scratched."

"Once they lock onto that scent you just help them and encourage them as much as you can."

Euchre even helped to guard the Pope and the Queen of England during visits to Canada. In all, he was just about the perfect example of a good police dog. And he was more than that: on a cool, mid-April Saturday early in his career, Euchre became a hero.

Constable Killens and Euchre had not been working together for long when the call came in. A seventeen-year-old boy was missing in the bush near Crosby, Ontario. The boy, Christian, had his dog, Spud, with him. He was visiting from Montreal, and didn't know the area at all. No one knew where he had gone. As well, Christian had health problems and it was very important that he be found quickly. A massive search was organized.

Constable Killens and Euchre, as well as another officer and his dog, were called in around six o'clock that night to help with the search. It was about five degrees Celsius, and foggy, with a light drizzle falling.

"So foggy you couldn't see in front of you,"

Constable Killens says, "so I knew I was going to have trouble finding Christian."

The fog that made it hard to see, however, helped Euchre. Fog means moisture, and the more moisture there is in the air, the easier it is to track. Tracker dogs are so highly skilled they can follow rafts in the water, and even flakes of human skin or tiny threads that fall off clothing. They can track right through towns and into the country, following scents that are days old. Even so, it was late evening by now, and the trail was getting cold. Euchre needed all the help he could get.

With Euchre on his three-metre tether, the officers and their dogs began searching for scent. They searched through the night and on into the next morning. If Euchre got off on a wrong scent, they would just return and try again.

"We work and use every advantage we can," Constable Killens says. "We go to spots where no one else has gone. I was working downwind of where we thought the boy was, so this was working to my advantage."

By three-thirty Sunday morning more searchers were called in, including a helicopter and a third dog. Many local volunteers were among those trying desperately to locate Christian during that long, cold night.

The search finally ended about ten o'clock that morning, when Euchre picked Christian's scent off the wind.

"Once they lock onto that scent you just help them and encourage them as much as you can," Constable Killens says. He did just that, and suddenly looked up to find Christian, cold and shivering, standing in front of him.

"How are you?" he asked.

"F-fine," the boy managed to get out.

Christian and Spud were taken back to a very grateful family. In spite of the cold and exposure, Christian had survived with no lasting ill effects.

"We find about two people a year who would have died otherwise, on average," Constable Killens says. "Finding a lost person is everything you work for. I've got the best job in the OPP."

Constable Killens works with another dog now, since Euchre died. Euchre worked faithfully for Constable Killens and the Ontario Provincial Police for almost six years — a long time in the life of a career dog.

Sam with Phyllis McLeod

SAM

The Dog Who Remembered

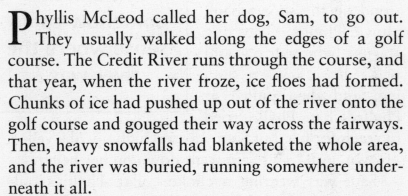

Phyllis McLeod called her dog, Sam, to go out. They usually walked along the edges of a golf course. The Credit River runs through the course, and that year, when the river froze, ice floes had formed. Chunks of ice had pushed up out of the river onto the golf course and gouged their way across the fairways. Then, heavy snowfalls had blanketed the whole area, and the river was buried, running somewhere underneath it all.

"I wonder where that river is flowing today," Phyllis said to Sam as they started out. The water was having to find a new path every day under the snow because of the ice build-up.

Phyllis couldn't see any trace of where the river might be. It was a beautiful day, even if it was cold. The sun was bouncing off the snow like diamonds. It was such a gorgeous morning, Phyllis let Sam off the leash to run free. Then, all of a sudden, she felt the ground beneath her give way. The river had found Phyllis — and she was falling into it.

The water was freezing cold, and the current was fast. Phyllis grabbed at an ice floe in front of her, but she could feel her whole body being pulled under. She couldn't put her feet on the bottom — the current was far too strong. Phyllis hung on with every bit of her strength. She knew that if she let go she would be dragged under the ice, and no one would find her until spring.

It seemed to Phyllis that she clung there for an eternity, but it was probably only a few seconds until Sam came back. She stood on the snowy bank above Phyllis. The dog started whimpering and w h i n - ing, and then pulled at Phyllis's hat. Phyllis tried

> **"I think she somehow could sense where the river was."**

to reach for her, but Sam was too high up. She yelled, "Down, girl!" and Sam went down on her belly.

Sam was wearing a choke collar. Phyllis's only chance was to grab for it, but the dog was still almost out of reach.

What if I miss? Phyllis thought, but she was slipping further and further under the ice. There was no other way. With one hand still clinging to the ice floe, she lunged forward and up, grabbing for Sam.

Her fingers closed around the metal collar.

"Pull, girl!" Phyllis shouted.

Sam stood back upon her four legs, braced herself, and pulled. She pulled Phyllis right out of the water and up onto the ice.

"I just hugged her, and lay there, trying to get my breath," Phyllis recalls. "Then I had to walk back home — a good half-hour away. I was afraid I might fall into the river again, because, except for the spot where I fell in, I still didn't know where it was running."

Phyllis put Sam back on the leash and let her lead the way.

"She kind of picked her way around, and I just followed her. I think she somehow could sense where the river was." Phyllis arrived home nearly frozen — but she made it, thanks to Sam.

How did Sam know what "Pull!" meant? To answer that question, Phyllis had to remember back to when Sam was a puppy.

"We've always had dogs, but never a German Shepherd," Phyllis says, "and I had always dreamed of having one. So, for my son Ian's twenty-first birthday, my other two sons and I went shopping and bought this puppy. She was so small, she could fit into the palm of my hand. We all just fell in love with her."

Ian was at university at the time — actually, he didn't really want a dog! — so Sam became Phyllis's dog. She wanted to call the dog Baby or Princess, but the rest of her family laughed at her. "You can't go out at night and call, 'Here, Baby! Here, Baby!'" they said. Phyllis's husband started calling the dog Sam, and soon so did the rest of the family. When they went to register her at the vet's, they were told Sam was a male name. They registered her as Lady Samantha, but she's always been just Sam at home.

Sam was an amazing pup and easy to train, Phyllis

says. She was very intelligent and a "wonderful, wonderful pet," although she grew very quickly into a huge dog. When anyone came to the front door, she just assumed that they were there to visit her, and she would wiggle and make all kinds of welcoming noises.

Not everyone appreciated the welcome, especially those who didn't particularly like dogs. In fact, Phyllis's sons found it downright annoying sometimes.

"When they were teenagers and tried to sneak in late at night, Phyllis laughs, "she'd greet them at the door, and the noise of her tail banging against the stair railing would wake up the whole family. I always knew exactly what time they came in."

The only thing Sam was afraid of was thunderstorms. She ran out of the yard once during a particularly bad one, onto the four-lane highway that runs near the McLeod home. A driver thought he had hit her when she ran right in front of him, so he jammed on his brakes and jumped out to see if she was all right. Sam took the opportunity to leap into his car for safety from the storm and wouldn't get out. He ended up taking her to the pound, where Phyllis found her.

Sam was great with children. If someone came over with a baby, she would lie down beside him or her, and if the baby cried, Sam would go over to the mother and pull on her clothes, as if to say, "Hey! Your baby's crying!" Sam loved to play, and it is when recalling Sam's favourite games that Phyllis thinks of something.

"When she was a pup, she had this big rubber dog bone with a ring at one end that a person could hang onto. My sons would play with her with it. She would grab onto it — and you know how a Shepherd's jaws lock — and they would say 'Pull, girl, pull.' She'd tug and hang onto it so hard they could swing her right off her feet. That was when she was a pup, though. Sam was seven years old when she rescued me, but she must have remembered somehow."

Sadly, Sam died just months after receiving the Ralston Purina Award for her bravery.

"She had a beautiful, gentle nature," Phyllis says. "There was a very strong bond between Sam and me. She seemed to sense my moods. If I was down, she'd just be there for me. She was a character. A wonderful character."

Patsy and Daisy

PATSY

The Kindly Cat

T his short-haired brown tabby with orange colouring is about nine months old. She is very friendly and would make an ideal pet." That's how the ad for "This Week's Pet" ran in the newspaper. The Seiler family was looking for a friendly cat, and they'd been told that calicoes and tabbies were the friendliest, so they decided to go have a look.

What they had heard was true. Of all the cats at the Smith's Falls animal shelter, the young tabby definitely had the friendliest face, four-year-old Sonja decided. The family took the cat home with them and named her Patsy (although Sonja immediately nicknamed her Pumpkin Face because of her orange colouring). The Seilers never did find out where Patsy had come from, but her thick, heavy fur hinted that she was an outdoor cat.

Everything was new to the young cat in the Seiler home, and at first she was a bit scared. Perhaps it was the first time she'd ever been part of a family. But Sonja and her younger sister, Monika, loved and cared for her, and it wasn't long until Patsy settled in.

"She really loved being rubbed on her stomach and would purr and purr," Sonja says. When the sisters tried dressing her up in doll clothes, however, she wouldn't stand for it. Patsy was much too dignified for that! She was independent and very good at catching mice. But she was also very affectionate.

Six years after Patsy came, Daisy joined the family. Daisy was one of a litter of kittens born on the farm next door. She was a calico cat — another friendly one. Patsy adopted and loved Daisy right from the start. Good mouser that she was, she kept the kitten well supplied with mice.

Daisy didn't mind being dressed up in doll clothes. Sonja calls her a Gumby cat because she'll let herself be twisted into almost any shape, just like the bendable character of that name. In the winter, she'll curl around the girls' necks like a scarf — Sonja can even wear her like a belt. But Daisy wasn't a placid kitten. From the start, she was very good at climbing trees and getting up in the girls' tree fort. "She loves climbing," Sonja says. "She walks on the smallest branches. She's like a daredevil. She does flips up there."

Sonja and Monika's father, Dieter, is allergic to cats, so he built houses in the garage for Patsy and Daisy. The two boxes are insulated and heated with a battery warmer. The garage itself has lots of beams for cats to climb and jump off. One of Daisy's favourite tricks is leaping onto the sloping windshield of their van and sliding down it. Dieter Seiler also constructed a solar house on the front patio for the cats. It is a wooden box with one slanted, Plexiglas side. When the sun is out, it's as warm as toast in there.

No matter how cozy, the cats sprang from the solar house when Sonja and Monika came outside, especially in the morning when the girls walked up the road to meet the school bus. The cats waited with the girls until the bus came, and often came tearing up the driveway to greet them when they got off the bus in the afternoon.

One morning in early spring, when she was still a kitten, Daisy decided she was tired from the walk to the school-bus stop. She curled up just where she was and fell asleep, the way that kittens do. Patsy was off in the bushes, exploring, and Sonja and Monika were talking as they waited. The bus loomed over the rise in the

> **"She walks on the smallest branches. She's like a daredevil."**

country road, and the girls got ready. Then they noticed Daisy, sleeping peacefully — right in the path of the bus.

"Daisy, Daisy!" Sonja screamed. But the kitten just slept on.

Out of the bushes streaked Patsy. With a rush, she charged at the kitten, dashing almost under the wheels of the bus, and chased it out of the road to safety!

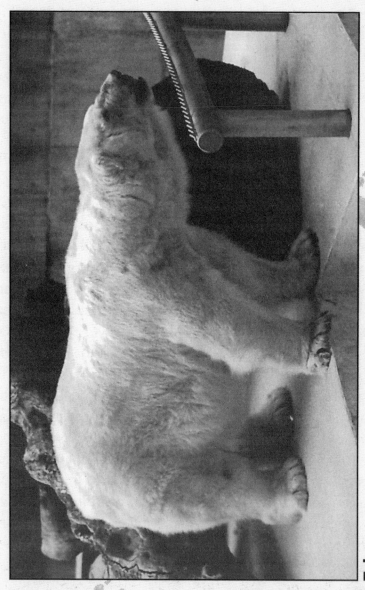

Tuk

TUK

The Heroic Polar Bear

Tuk lived more than thirty-five years at the Stanley Park Zoo in Vancouver, far longer than any polar bear would in the wild, and almost the longest of any polar bear in captivity. He spent most of his time lying in the sun sleeping, nose twitching at the occasional fly. Looking at him in his old age, you would never have imagined that years ago, when he was a young bear, he saved a life.

He was brought as a cub to the Stanley Park Zoo in 1961, along with three other polar bear cubs. A special Polar Bear Grotto was built just for them at the zoo, and they settled in. It was the best Polar Bear Grotto the zoo could build at that time. Mike Mackintosh, the head of Wildlife Services for the City of Vancouver, came to work at the zoo as a student volunteer when the bears were about five years old. He got to know them very well. There were two other males besides Tuk, Old Man and Grump, and a female, Lady.

When the bears were young, they used to play

together. They were in and out of the pool all the time, running around, diving in, tumbling all over, and shoving each other. When they slept, they would lie together in one big ball in the central den.

"But they all had their own unique personalities," Mike says. Grump was the biggest, weighing nearly 500 kilograms, but Old Man was the boss. Old Man was bothered for much of his life by arthritis, and was quite a bit slower than the others, but there was no doubt that he was in charge.

Grump was Mike Mackintosh's personal favourite. "He was all roar and no action," Mike says. "He was a very active bear and in outstanding physical condition. He could stand and touch his nose to the top of the Bear Grotto, which was almost four metres high. Kids watching him would just gasp in awe. We'd toss fish to him,

> **"Polar bears can't be trained. You'll never see one in a circus."**

and when he stood and put his feet up against the sides to support himself while catching them, it was incredible how much space those feet would cover."

"As big as dinner plates," Graham Ford, the assistant manager at the zoo, describes Grump's feet.

"He was a very, very interesting bear," Mike says. "I was really fond of him."

Lady was the most predatory of the group. "Of all the bears, I considered her the most untrustworthy," Mike says. "I used to think that in spite of the fact that she was the smallest of the bears, if any one of them was going to eat me, it would be her." She was quite aggressive. When she wanted something, she didn't hesitate to tell the others off, even Old Man.

Mike describes Tuk as the "serendipity bonzo" of the group, a bit of a prankster and rather a free spirit by polar bear standards. "One of his favourite jokes was to lunge at people coming into the feeding den. Standing quietly off to one side, he would wait until someone had walked up close to the bars. Then he'd suddenly leap forward, rather like a dog might." Mike and his co-workers played along. They would bring visitors, especially kids, in to watch the bears feeding, and smile as Tuk made them gasp and jump away.

It may have been play, but the keepers were glad there were bars between them and the bear. They would sometimes pat him through the bars, but they had to be careful. "You never know when you're going to lose a finger," says Graham. "Polar bears can't be trained. You'll never see one in a circus. They're more ferocious than other bears." Tuk lived in a zoo nearly all his life, but he was not tame. He was not a pet.

One sunny summer day, there was the usual crowd of people, mostly children, around the Bear Grotto. The bears had just been let out for the morning, after being fed. Tuk was lying on the parapet overhanging their big pool. He was sprawled out on his stomach, dozing lazily in the sun. Suddenly two young men came running by. As they ran past, one of them reached underneath his jacket, pulled something out, and threw it into the pool. To the horror of everybody around, a young kitten hit the water with a splash and sank below the surface. Everyone screamed.

Tuk woke up. He opened one eye and looked over the edge of the pool. The kitten was just a small blob under water. Tuk stood up and stretched, and the people around the grotto held their breath. Did the little kitten look like dessert to the massive bear? Tuk yawned, then he slid into the water. Children screamed again. A few seconds later, Tuk surfaced. The tiny cat was pinned delicately between Tuk's front teeth by the nape of its neck, just the way a mother cat would carry her kitten. Tuk swam to the edge of the pool and hauled himself out, dripping water. Still holding the kitten carefully in his teeth, he lumbered back up onto the parapet. Then he lay down. He held the kitten down with his enormous paws, opened his huge mouth — and began to lick the tiny creature dry.

The other bears were beginning to take notice, and they didn't look as friendly as Tuk. The zookeepers frantically tried to get the bears separated. It took well over an hour, but finally they got all except Tuk inside. It took a while longer to convince Tuk to leave the kitten and go inside the pen as well, but at last they succeeded. The little kitten was fetched out of the grotto and taken home by one of the volunteer workers.

Tuk lived to be the last of the four polar bears at the Stanley Park Zoo. Polar bears are by nature very solitary animals, and Tuk didn't seem to mind being alone. In fact, he seemed happier without Lady bossing him around. The zoo closed in 1995, and the other animals relocated, but not Tuk. He was too old to be moved someplace new. So, the grotto stayed as long as Tuk lived.

The Yangtze Incident

A civil war raged throughout China between the years 1946 and 1949. After the end of the Second World War, two parties began their struggle for control of the country. The Nationalist Party was led by Chiang Kai-shek; the Communist Party was led by Mao Tsetung.

Britain was a neutral country — the British government wasn't supporting one party or the other — and maintained an embassy office at Nanking on the Yangtze River. In spite of Britain's neutrality, in April of 1949 the captain and crew of a British frigate, HMS *Amethyst,* found themselves right in the middle of the battle. . . .

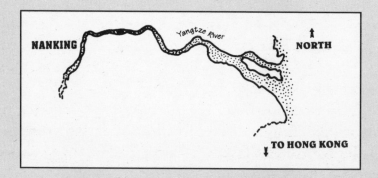

SIMON

The Ship's Cat

Simon

S imon, a black and white tomcat, was found as a kitten on Stonecutters' Island, off Hong Kong. He was brought on board the *Amethyst,* a British navy frigate that was stationed there, and was given the very important job of catching rats that tried to sneak aboard.

The cat soon became the crew's pet and mascot. He was a favourite especially with the younger seamen, and of Boy Seaman First Class Sid Horton in particular. At seventeen, Sid was the youngest on board. He had been in the navy since he was just a little over fifteen years old, and had never been in battle. That changed on April 20, 1949, one week after Sid joined the *Amethyst* crew.

Early that morning, the *Amethyst* was making its way up the Yangtze River in China, carrying supplies for the British Embassy at Nanking. The mist swirled over the ship's wake as it churned through the murky waters. On the north shore of the river was the

Communist People's Liberation Army, with guns and heavy artillery (cannon) aimed across the river at the Nationalist Army of Chiang Kai-shek, positioned on the south bank.

Because Britain was not supporting one army or the other, the *Amethyst*'s captain, Lieutenant-Commander B.M. Skinner, expected safe passage. Still, he knew he should make his way through the fighting zone with caution. The Chinese Communists had already shot at the Nationalists on the south bank, and the *Amethyst* had to pass right between them.

At first the heavy fog cloaked the ship, but as the sun rose, the heat burned it off. The crew was tense and alert. At twenty minutes past nine, flame suddenly erupted from the north shore and a shell whined overhead. Seconds later it exploded, ripping apart the wheelhouse. The man at the wheel was hit and fell to one side, dragging the wheel to the left with him. The ship turned toward shore.

The *Amethyst* began to fight back, and the battle raged on for hours. Finally, after noon, the Communist guns fell silent. The crew of the *Amethyst* could take stock. Of 183 crew members, 23 were dead or dying and 31 were wounded, including the captain and his senior officers. The ship was so damaged that it was unsteerable. (It was found later that the ship had been hit fifty-three times.) It plowed into the mud of Rose Island, off the south bank, and stuck fast. As the lull in the fighting continued, the officers tried to move the ship out of the mud. They were successful, and managed to move the ship about a kilometre upriver. But every time they tried to make a break for safety, the Communists fired at them.

In all the confusion, no one had had time to think of Simon. But when things calmed down, Simon appeared. He was bleeding from a shrapnel wound, his fur was singed, his face burned. No one knew for certain what had happened to him, but his favourite sleeping place was on the captain's bed, and a shell had exploded in that cabin, knocking a hole in the hull right beside it.

The little cat hadn't lost his spirit, though. Rubbing affectionately against the legs of his friends as they assembled for a makeshift meal, he avidly wolfed down all the scraps they gave him. Sid Horton was especially glad to see that Simon had survived. (He himself had suffered a broken arm.) As he lay in his hammock that night, Sid heard scrabbling along the steam pipes that ran over his head. A rat scurried by, closely pursued by a sure-footed cat. Wounded or not, Simon was back on the job.

And Simon stayed on the job — for the next 101 days, as the *Amethyst* lay trapped in the Yangtze River. The men were able to trade with the villagers on shore for eggs, cabbages and other fresh vegetables, but even these were scanty. In spite of strict rationing, food began to run dangerously low. In the meantime, the daytime heat was sweltering and the rats multiplied at an alarming rate. But Simon kept pace with them. Although still suffering the after-effects of his wounds and burns, for three months he caught at least a rat a day — even though some of the rats were bigger than he was.

The *Amethyst* finally escaped on the last day of

July. The captain planned the break-out carefully. In the dark of night he slipped anchor and the *Amethyst* quietly began its run. It was a wild, almost blind sprint. The Yangtze was a river full of twists, turns and shoals, and no one aboard knew its waters. All the captain and crew had to navigate by was a set of charts which might be out of date. But bravely, making smoke for cover and weaving desperately to avoid the shells being fired at them, they dashed for freedom.

It was more than 200 kilometres to the mouth of the Yangtze. They made it just as the first rays of dawn were lightening the sky. News of their heroic exploit travelled fast, and the story of Simon, the Ship's Cat, travelled with it. When the men returned to Hong Kong, newspaper reporters and photographers were there to greet them. Sid Horton was given the honour of holding the cat for all the pictures the media wanted.

Simon was declared a hero. Back in England, he was awarded the Dickin Medal — the highest honour for animals — in recognition of his bravery under fire and for "disposing of many rats though wounded by a shell blast." He is buried now in Ilford, Essex, and the inscription on his tombstone reads:

"In Memory of Simon. Served in HMS *Amethyst* May 1948–November 1949. Throughout the Yangtze Incident his behaviour was of the highest order."

THE DICKIN MEDAL

Many animals have performed heroic feats in war. Some have been awarded medals. The Dickin Medal is awarded to animals who displayed gallantry during WWII and its aftermath. Fifty-three Dickin Medals have been awarded, 18 of which were presented to dogs, 3 to horses, 1 to a cat, and 31 to pigeons.

GANDER

During the invasion of Hong Kong in 1941, a big "Newf" named Gander saved the lives of several Canadian soldiers. He picked up a live hand grenade and ran away with it in his mouth until it exploded. He was awarded the Dickin Medal.

Ricky

RICKY

The Pet Who Went to War

Dogs have gone to war since the days of the Egyptian Pharaohs thousands of years ago. Even before that, they guarded the caves of Stone Age people and hunted with them. Packs of ferocious hounds accompanied the Persians when they conquered Egypt in 526 B.C. War dogs, wearing spiked collars and chain mail, fought beside the soldiers of Rome. Right up to modern times, dogs have had their part to play in the wars that people fought. Mostly, these dogs were big and fierce, trained to kill.

In the Second World War, however, a new breed of war dog came into being. The British army desperately needed guard dogs. They also needed scouting dogs to help the soldiers move safely into enemy territory, dogs to carry messages, and ambulance dogs to pull carts and stretchers. They needed thousands of dogs, in fact, and they didn't have them. So they appealed to the people of Britain to lend their pets.

The people responded, and dogs began to arrive at military headquarters all over the country. Among

59

them was Ricky, a Welsh Sheepdog, who belonged to Mr. and Mrs. Litchfield of Bromley. Ricky was sent to serve with the mine-detecting platoon of the British army.

Dogs were very valuable to mine detectors. They had found that a dog was usually too light in weight to trigger off a mine. Dogs, along with their handlers, could be sent ahead of advancing troops to sniff out the mines safely. The platoon was soon training dogs by the hundreds. Gradually, it began to look like a dog show around there. No animals were ever treated better, and the dogs were in top condition. They were intensely enthusiastic about their work.

Ricky took to the change from pampered pet to army dog immediately. He was trained using the reward system — a biscuit for him every time he sniffed out a buried mine — and was soon collecting his share of the treats.

In 1944, Ricky was landed in Europe as War Dog 6883, attached to the Royal Engineers, and kept by Sergeant Yelding of the Royal Army Veterinary Corps. Now he was working for real, helping to clear mines off roads and railway tracks while the battle went on around him. On December 3 of that year, he was working in Nederwent, Holland, clearing the edges of a canal bank. One by one, he found all the mines.

Then one exploded. The section commander nearest to Ricky fell, injured by the blast. Ricky himself was bleeding from a wound in the head. But Ricky kept right on working. Without the least bit of fuss, ignoring the blood, he found a path through the mines. Through that path the section commander was brought to safety. Then, he and Ricky both received medical treatment.

Ricky received the Dickin Medal. It was inscribed "For Gallantry, We Also Serve." The Royal Society for the Prevention of Cruelty to Animals awarded him the "For Valour" medal and a certificate, on which was written: "For outstanding ability, courage and devotion to duty while on active service with the British Landing Armies, from D-Day to the cessation of hostilities during the World War, 1939–45."

Ricky did such good work during the war and established such a good reputation for himself that, after the war, the War Office offered to buy him from his owners. Mr. and Mrs. Litchfield did not accept the offer, though. They were too glad to have him back home, safe and sound after all his adventures.

Lindy with David and Margaret Downie

LINDY

Who Made a Lucky Choice

It was a crisp November afternoon when David Downie set out for a walk with his dog, Lindy. He got only about seven metres away from his home when he suddenly suffered an attack of angina and fell, unconscious, into the snow.

Lindy, leash trailing, set out for help. She ran past several townhouses in the neighbourhood, then came across a man and woman in a car, backing out of a driveway. Lindy started to run back and forth behind the car, not letting them move. The woman in the car got out and picked up Lindy's leash, intending to get her out of the way. Immediately, Lindy began to pull her toward the spot where David Downie lay.

By the way the dog was acting, the woman realized something was wrong. She let the dog lead her and found David. By this time, David was vomiting blood. But the woman didn't panic. She knew just what to do. She turned David onto his side so that he wouldn't choke, then told her husband to call 9-1-1. She covered David up with a sleeping bag to protect him from the cold. It was fortunate for David that Lindy had picked the perfect person to help her master: Eleanor Craig, who just happened to be a registered nurse.

In the meantime, a neighbour passing by recognized Lindy. He took her home and alerted David's wife. David came back to consciousness briefly as they loaded him into the ambulance. The next thing he remembers is waking up in the hospital with his wife at his side.

> **"She never complained . . . She was a good dog."**

"We like to joke about the clever choice Lindy made in finding a registered nurse to help me," David Downie says now. "But we know that Lindy's very special and we'll be forever grateful to her."

David and his wife, Margaret, got Lindy when she was about a year old. Some people who wanted to get rid of their dog put an ad in the newspaper, and David and Margaret saw it. When they went to look at her, Lindy was outside, tied to a stake on the lawn. David asked if he could take the dog out for a walk. The people told him she'd never been for a walk.

"She was over a year old, and she'd never even been for a walk!" David says with disgust. "She'd obviously been abused. She would cower every time you so much as looked at her." He and Margaret felt sorry for the dog and took her home with them. They set about the task of teaching her to trust people again. Luckily for David, Lindy learned.

Lindy never did learn to be obedient, though. "She's a Border Collie/Basset Hound mix, and that's the Basset Hound characteristic," David explains. "If you called her, she'd go the other way. She'd go around in a big circle, and eventually come, but her own way, and in her own time. We went to Basset Hound trials once, and even there they wandered all over the place. So we didn't feel so badly because Lindy wasn't obedient."

Lindy loved David and Margaret's grandchildren. They used to come over, and she liked nothing better than playing with them.

Lindy was awarded the Ralston Purina Animal Hall of Fame Medal. Sadly, at the same time she developed cancer. David and Margaret left her with their family veterinarian while they went to Toronto to accept the award for her. Ralston gave them a beautiful painting of Lindy, so they have that to remember her by, and her picture was in the *Winnipeg Sun,* looking as happy and bright as ever, even though it was taken while she was sick.

"She never complained, all through her illness. She was a good dog," David says.

And a dog who more than repaid the kindness that David and Margaret showed to her.

Samantha with Donald Holmes

SAMANTHA

The Motherly Dog

There was a dog at the stable where Alana Tintse rode. The dog was a German Shepherd, possibly mixed with a bit of Husky. The people who ran the stable had found her — she was either lost or abandoned. Although she was friendly, they didn't really want the timid, cowering dog around. Alana's coach was on the point of taking the dog to the Society for the Prevention of Cruelty to Animals (SPCA) shelter, but Alana was determined to find a home for her. Unable to take the dog herself, she asked some friends, Brian and Michelle Holmes, if they would take the dog in.

"Oh, sure," said Michelle. "We'll take another dog." They named her Samantha.

The Holmes already had a dog, Monty, a mixed-breed pup. At first Samantha seemed determined to lose him. She would lead Monty off on long explorations — and happily return home without him. Brian Holmes had many a call to go and fetch him back. But around the time Monty figured out how to find his own way home, Samantha's mothering instincts kicked in. She became very protective of him, and the two dogs are always together now.

When the Holmes family dogsits a friend's Yorkshire Terrier and Llasa Apso, Samantha is in her glory looking after the two small dogs. She found Whoopi, the Yorkshire Terrier, once when she was lost in the woods. "Mind you," says Brian, "I think at first Samantha thought Whoopi was a squirrel!" She is even gentle with Brian's chickens and ducks.

Samantha is especially fond of children. When Brian takes her along in his truck into town and she sees children playing at recess in a schoolyard, she goes wild wanting to get out and play with them. Any child who comes to visit is welcomed and well licked, and the four Holmes grandchildren are special favourites.

One day Brian was home alone working on his computer. Monty was in the house with him. Brian heard Monty barking and went to the door to see if anyone had driven up. What he saw was Samantha with a little child hanging on to her, his arms wrapped around her neck. When Samantha saw Brian, she stopped, turned around, and started to lick the child. Brian grabbed his coat.

It was February, the snow was deep, and the temperature was hovering around ten degrees below zero, with a wicked wind. The child was dressed only in a light jacket, unbuttoned, and with no hat. He had mittens, but they were hanging on strings beside his bare hands. He wasn't crying, but he was shaking with cold.

Brian looked around. There was nobody else there.

He tried to find out the boy's name, but couldn't make out what he was saying. Again, he looked around, trying to see if there was an adult anywhere near. He even ran quickly down his own long driveway, thinking that, because it was so icy out, a car might have slid into the ditch.

The only car he found was a little yellow battery-operated car, a child's ride-on toy, abandoned out on the snowy road. Brian picked it up and put it in his driveway where it could be seen from the road, then hurried to get the boy inside the house.

Once inside, he took the boy's jacket off and started rubbing his hands. The child accepted Brian's help trustingly, and soon began to warm up. The cookie Brian gave him helped too. Brian kept asking questions. He thought the boy said his name was Ronald, then gradually made out that the boy was going "to see Mommy and the new baby."

Brian called the Ontario Provincial Police. By the time they arrived, a very worried father had also turned up.

It seemed that three-year-old Donald — that was actually his name — had woken early that morning and had decided to take his battery-operated car to the hospital where his mother and new baby sister were. He dressed himself as well as he could — even managed to get his boots on — and set out while his dad was still asleep. The little car's batteries died about a kilometre away from home, right at Brian and Michelle Holmes' driveway.

No one knows for certain what happened then, but Samantha, who was outside, found him. Donald must have grabbed onto her for warmth and comfort, and she pulled him home to Brian.

The OPP reported to Brian the next day that the child was suffering from hypothermia (a dangerous lowering of his body's inner temperature). The area around the Holmes's house is fairly isolated, and if Samantha hadn't found Donald, he might well have died. The police were pleased to have a story with such a happy ending to report, and they sent out a press release. Reporters and camera crews were quick to arrive, and Samantha became famous. She was on CBC *Radio Noon,* on television, and in all the area papers. That spring she was selected to receive the Ontario SPCA "Hero of the Year" award.

And Donald's mother has promised to keep the motherly dog supplied with dog biscuits for the rest of her life.

PIG TO THE RESCUE

In November 1995, Snort, a pot-bellied pig from Oregon, saved his owners, Deb and Collin Stolpe, from carbon monoxide poisoning when he woke them up with his squealing, snorting and running around. "It's kind of embarrassing to have a pig save your life," says Collin, "but I thank God she was there that night 'cause I have a lot of living left."

Freddy

The Santa Dog

The Grand Marshal of the Edmonton Santa Claus Parade in 1994 wore a dark grey coat. He was small, with curly hair. His name was Freddy; he was a hero, and he was a dog. He had saved his owner Sylvana Burnette's life in a most unusual way.

Sylvana had come to Canada from England three years before. One of the saddest things she had to do was leave her dog, Rambo, behind, although she left him in a good home with a friend. Once she was settled in Edmonton, she began to look for another dog. She scanned the newspaper ads every day, hoping to find a Yorkshire Terrier puppy to take the place of Rambo. There didn't seem to be any ads for Yorkies, but one day she saw a notice from someone searching for a home for their five-year-old Maltese–Poodle cross.

"It seemed sad that an older dog like that had to leave the home he grew up in, and I wondered why," says Sylvana. She didn't want an older dog, and she wanted a Yorkie, but she called the owner of the dog, just out of curiosity. She found out that the dog's owner had remarried, and the dog and the new husband didn't get along. "After thinking about that poor little thing for a while — if they didn't find a home for him he would go to the pound — I thought, maybe we could just help each other here. I could give him the home he needed, and he could end my yearning for a 'furry friend,'" Sylvana says. She went to see the dog, and Freddy came home with her.

> **"Suddenly, we felt the ground shaking and a noise like thunder."**

By the second day, he seemed to realize that he was there for good, and he settled right down. Soon, Freddy was Sylvana's shadow, following her everywhere. "He's a very intelligent dog," she says. "You have to spell out words like walk and food." Sylvana laughs. "And he can tell you exactly what he wants all the time. He taught himself to get up on his hind legs and dance around in a circle whenever he wants a treat."

Sylvana and her husband, Allan, take Freddy everywhere. He loves it when they go camping in the summers, and he especially loves the water. One time he got a shock. They were camping on Elk Island and had driven around to see the buffalo that roam free there. Later, when they were going for a walk in the woods, Freddy ran ahead of them up the trail and started barking at something around the bend.

"Suddenly, we felt the ground shaking and a noise like thunder. Back around the bend raced Freddy, and he did a flying leap into my arms. We realized he'd picked on a buffalo! We ran and hid behind a tree until the great big thing went thundering by. It was good for us that the wind was blowing toward us or it would have smelled us. Stupid dog," Sylvana adds, affectionately.

Freddy has all kinds of toys — fluffy bears, balls, and chew sticks — but his favourite possession is a baby blanket. He stuffs it in his mouth when he goes to sleep. It's the only thing he will not let anyone take from him. Sylvana says she has a real job trying to wash it. She has to put Freddy out in the yard and then sneak the blanket into the washing machine.

One summer day in the middle of August, Sylvana was feeling hot and sticky and decided to take a refreshing bath. She poured her favourite peach bath oil into the water, filled the tub to the brim, then lay back to relax. Sylvana has asthma, and sometimes hot baths can trigger an attack. She started wheezing, and knew she should get her medication. She remembers thinking, "Boy, is this bathroom ever getting steamed up!" as she tried to stand. Then, she fainted.

> "I don't know how he did it, but he did. I was stunned."

The next thing she remembers is waking up, coughing, still in the bathtub. Freddy was in there, too, jumping all over her. Sylvana pushed him away. "Get off me, you silly dog!" she said. Then she realized there was no water in the tub. She looked over at Freddy and saw he had the bathtub plug in his mouth. Somehow or other, Freddy must have jumped into the tub after Sylvana fainted and pulled out the plug!

"He saved my life," Sylvana says. "I must have gone under the water because my hair was soaking wet, I had a mouthful of bath oil, and there was a bump on the back of my head. I don't know how he did it, but he did. I was stunned."

When the news got around, Freddy made the front page of the local newspaper, complete with photographs. Radio and TV shows in Canada and the United States were on the phone for interviews. Freddy was a star! The culmination of all the attention was the invitation to

"I guess I saved his life. And in return, he saved mine."

be the Grand Marshal of the Edmonton Santa Claus Parade. They dressed Freddy up in a Santa Claus suit with reindeer antlers, and he and Sylvana led the parade, sitting in a bright red bathtub.

Freddy is still famous. When Sylvana takes him for walks, people crowd around him. Gifts for him arrive in the mail every day, especially from children. People shower him with treats and food. So much, in fact, that Sylvana has had to put him on a strict diet — he was getting fat.

"I truly believe that Freddy was meant to come into our lives to do the wonderful and heroic thing he did," Sylvana says. "He probably would have gone to the pound if it hadn't been for me, so I guess I saved his life. And in return, he saved mine."

Nellie with Ken Emerson

NELLIE

The Dog Who Knew What To Do

Nellie is a big black and tan German Shepherd with gentle eyes. She's had a litter of nine pure-bred pups, and one unexpected romance with a dog that jumped through the window. She used to belong to Ken Emerson's grandson, but when he got married and moved into town, Ken took Nellie home. He's a tobacco farmer, and there's lots of room for Nellie to run where he lives. Nellie had known Ken and his wife Pauline for a long time, even stayed with them when their grandson visited, so she didn't mind the change. She loves to go with Ken on his trips around the farm. Lucky for him — because this probably saved his life.

One afternoon Ken came home about two-thirty, after a meeting in the community. He wanted to check the irrigation dam on his property because there were plans for another dam up above it. The going was rough, so he decided to take the tractor. He scribbled a quick note to Pauline telling her what time it was, where he was going, and that he'd be back shortly. As he started up the tractor, Nellie trotted up, tail wagging expectantly. He almost told her to stay, then changed his mind. It would be a good run for her.

After checking the dam, Ken went around to the back end of the farm to see if there was any switchgrass coming up in the summer fallow. There was a log across the road to discourage trespassers, so he pulled off the road and took a detour around it. This meant going up a fairly steep incline. As he started up the hill, he felt the front end of the tractor lift.

"I let the tractor roll back and tried to hold it with the brakes," Ken said. "I thought the best thing to do would be to turn around and go down the hill head first, rather than try to back down."

But the front end caught, the tractor tipped and before he realized what was happening, Ken was thrown off. The tractor rolled right over him, then rolled over a couple more times until it reached the bottom of the hill.

> "I thought, somehow or other I've got to get word to Pauline, because I was back in where nobody would see me."

The next thing he knew, Ken was lying on the ground, alone in the sudden silence except for his dog. Strangely enough, he felt no pain. Nellie was sitting, looking at him, about ten metres away.

"I went to slide myself down the hill to her," Ken said, "but when I tried to move, my legs spread-eagled and I couldn't put them back together. I thought that maybe my right leg was broken, but I could hear the bones in my pelvis kind of grit together."

In shock, he still didn't feel any pain. Well, I'll crawl back to the road, thought Ken, hoping somebody would come along in an hour or so. But he soon realized he wasn't going to make it. Then he thought about Nellie.

"I thought, somehow or other I've got to get word to Pauline, because I was back in where nobody would see me. The only thing I could think of was to send something back with Nellie that they might recognize."

Ken always carries a jackknife, so he reached into his pocket and took it out, then started to cut up his shirt. It was a heavy shirt, and not easy to rip, but he finally managed to slit it up the seam to the pocket and cut a piece off.

"Nellie, come," he called.

The dog came up to him. He gave her a pat, and tied the shirt onto her collar. Then came the problem of how to make her understand what he needed her to do. Ken's grandson had obedience-trained Nellie. She would stay if told to, even "be nice" if other dogs were around, but Ken didn't know if she'd ever been taught the command to go home. He had to try, though. "Go home," he ordered.

Nellie moved about a metre away, looking worried, then sat down again.

"Go home!" Ken repeated.

She moved another metre away.

"Nellie, go home. Go home, Nellie!" he said as sternly as he could.

She got up, and with a last worried look at him, disappeared into the bushes.

"I figured, well, I guess I've done everything I can do," Ken says now.

After the dog left, Ken must have drifted in and out of consciousness. "Things went kind of grey," he says. He remembers staring at the cloudy, overcast sky. He remembers the ground being cold — so cold! — even though it was May. And he remembers ants.

"I would never have thought there'd be so many ants around," he says. They crawled all over him.

Pauline arrived home from shopping with her sister around four o'clock. She found Ken's note with the time at the top of it and was surprised that he wasn't back yet. She looked out the window and saw Nellie sitting up by the neighbours' house with what looked like a rag or something tied around her neck. She called the dog and untied the shirt, then called the neighbours to see if they had put it on her for some reason. When they assured her they hadn't, she looked more closely at the piece of cloth and recognized it as being cut from the shirt Ken had been wearing that day. She knew then that something was very wrong.

Neighbours banded together and followed the tractor tracks. Finally, they found Ken. They called an ambulance, and he was rushed to the hospital.

Ken was in hospital for four weeks with a broken pelvis and broken ribs. In spite of the doctors' verdict that it would take a long, long time to recuperate, he was out walking around within a week of leaving the hospital and has now made an almost complete recovery.

And Nellie? She was awarded the Ralston Purina Animal Hall of Fame Award for her bravery.

As far as Ken and Pauline know, Nellie had never heard the "go home" command before in her life. Yet she understood what Ken needed her to do. "She was sitting there watching me when I was trying to drag myself along," Ken says. "She knew there was something wrong with me." Ken was on the ground, badly hurt and suffering from shock and cold, for over two hours. If help hadn't come when it did, he might well have died.

"She got more cheese curds and baloney that day!" Pauline laughs.

RETRIEVED FROM THE ICE

On a wintery night in 1995, Jim Gilcrest took his two dogs — Tara, a rottweiler, and Tiree, a golden retriever — on a walk along a frozen Lake Simcoe. The ice gave way and Jim fell through. Tara raced back to his rescue, only to fall through as well. Tiree crouched on her belly and slowly crawled over until Jim could grab her and Tara could climb out over Jim. Then both dogs carefully pulled backwards until he was safe.

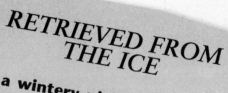

FLOYD

The Gentle Giant

Floyd with Glenn Murphy

I'd walk down the street and hear footsteps coming toward me. Then I'd hear them slowing down. Then I'd hear them go way around me — or even across the street."

Seeing Glenn Murphy's guide dog, Floyd, coming toward you on a narrow sidewalk, you'd likely make room, too. Floyd is one of the biggest German Shepherds you're ever likely to meet. Sitting at his ease, this dog could rest his nose quite comfortably on your dining room table, and from nose to tail he's almost as long as a bicycle.

Glenn got Floyd when he was a second year student at the University of Calgary. Because Glenn was in the middle of classes and couldn't take time off, the Canadian Guide Dogs for the Blind, located in Manotick, Ontario, flew Floyd and his trainer out to Glenn. There they went through an intensive three week training course. They used Glenn's own normal routes as their training ground, and soon Floyd knew the way to the bus stop, the bus route, and how to find, by name, every building that Glenn went to on campus.

Floyd learned the routines quickly and well, so well that he even worked out shortcuts to some of the buildings on his own. And despite his size, he proved to be very gentle. Glenn says, "He's the kind of dog you only have to speak softly to. If you ever raised your voice he'd get hurt really quickly. People thought he must be really hard to control, but he was so gentle on the hard handle [the special harness that guide dogs wear] and leash that with just a subtle command and a little flick of your fingers he worked beautifully.

> **"I really sometimes wonder what would have happened to me that night if Floyd hadn't got my mom up."**

"He is big, though," Glenn adds. "He decided to stand up and put his paws on my shoulders one day. I'm tall enough — about 5 foot 10 inches [175 centimetres] — but he was taller than me!"

Floyd learned very quickly that Glenn was his responsibility, and he was always protective. Glenn studies karate, and it was hard to convince Floyd that Glenn didn't need his protection when he was fighting. One evening it proved too much for Floyd. Glenn's friend Mike came over to where Glenn was sitting at a tournament one night, and gave him a friendly whack

on the shoulder with a rolled-up brochure. Big mistake.

In an instant, Glenn felt Floyd jump up, and he
heard his friend cry, "Glenn! Glenn!"

"What's going on?" Glenn asked.

"Your dog! Your dog!"

Glenn reached down. Floyd had Mike pinned
right to the ground. Mike is a big man, about a hundred kilograms, but Floyd wasn't letting him go anywhere. He wasn't biting Mike, but he had Mike's arm
in his mouth, right by the wrist where the rolled-up
paper was, and he wasn't letting him so much as
move. Glenn let the dog stand on his friend for a couple of minutes, then said, "Okay, Floyd." The dog let
Mike go. "I never trained him to do that," Glenn
adds. "He just did it, instinctively."

Glenn has good reason to be thankful for Floyd's
protective instinct, for it probably saved his life.
Guide dogs are heroic dogs every day of their lives —
every time a squirrel runs in front of their noses and
they don't chase it. But Floyd went one step further.

Glenn was boarding with his mother at the time.
One night, she was awakened by Floyd grabbing and
tugging at her arm. She got up and he pulled her
down to Glenn's bedroom. Glenn was lying on the
floor, unconscious and bleeding. She rushed to call
9-1-1; the paramedics and ambulance officers were
there within minutes.

Glenn was healthy and active, and had never
shown any signs of epilepsy. But that night, with no
warning, his body began to shake violently. As the
seizure went on, he fell out of bed and hit his head.

When the paramedics started working on Glenn, his mother tried to coax Floyd away, but the dog would have none of it. He broke away from her and returned to the bedside. Uneasy and more than a little scared, the paramedics let the dog stay only when they realized Glenn was blind and this was his guide dog. And over the next few days, while Glenn was recovering, Floyd rarely left his room.

Glenn had a concussion, and was out of school for a few weeks. The epilepsy was brought under control, but the seizure left him with a kind of amnesia. He was a month into the semester at university, but he had no memory at all of having attended classes. He went through the notes he had taped and then transcribed into Braille, and couldn't remember ever taking them.

"I never trained him to do that. He just did it, instinctively."

Glenn had to drop half his courses, and work on relearning everything he'd forgotten. He would not have had the courage to go back to school if it had not been for Floyd. "In fact, I couldn't have done it without Floyd," he says. "The walk to the bus, the long bus ride, and then getting around the campus — I would never have been able to do it if I had had to use a cane." During this difficult time, Floyd was not only Glenn's eyes, but his memory. There was always the fear of having another seizure in the street, too, but Glenn knew that he was safe with Floyd. The dog would never leave him.

"I really sometimes wonder what would have happened to me that night if Floyd hadn't got my mom up," Glenn says. "People sometimes die during seizures. Floyd just sort of stuck with me and never left my side, ever. He's a great dog."

Floyd is retired now, and Glenn has a new dog — a Labrador Retriever named Rusty. Floyd has fitted in beautifully with his new family, Dave and Audrey MacDonald and their teenage daughters, Lindsay and Holly. They couldn't love him more or be more proud of him. He has learned to relax and enjoy life — it's not unusual to see him lying in the sun on the front lawn with children all over him. His guide dog days are over and he's enjoying a well-earned rest — but he still walks Audrey carefully around puddles.

ANIMAL HEROES

From Playful Pup to Guide Dog

Guide dogs are carefully bred. When guide dog pups are six to eight weeks old, they are sent out to a foster home. There, for the next year or so, they live like normal dogs or almost like normal dogs. Their temporary owners give the dogs love and affection, but they know that these pups are being prepared for one of the most important careers a dog can have — guide dog for the blind. While they are still young, the foster-owners train the dogs to deal with all kinds of situations. The pups are walked on busy streets, taken on buses, trains and subways, into restaurants and through crowded malls. They are exposed to loud noises, sudden disturbances and exciting distractions. And they are encouraged to play with and tolerate children.

When the dogs are about fourteen months old they return to the guide dog centre where they undergo five to nine months of more intense training. Not all young dogs make it. The ones who do are finally ready to be matched up. Just as the dogs are carefully chosen, so are their potential owners. An applicant for a guide dog is screened very thoroughly.

Once an owner has been approved, the guide dog trainers select the dog they think is the right one. The blind person is brought to the centre to go through an intensive training course with his or her new canine partner. By the end, dog and human have bonded in a very special relationship.

Dogs can also be trained to be the hearing ears of a deaf person and to stand guard over or fetch help for someone having an epileptic seizure. They can even do all sorts of small jobs for people in wheelchairs. Helper dogs mean freedom and independence for their owners and they are the most faithful and loyal companions a human being could ever hope for.

Jiggs

JIGGS

A Champion in Every Way

It was a cold mid-winter day when the telephone rang at Toni and Lorry Emslie's Kadesh Kennels near Kemptville, Ontario. A four-year-old boy was lost. He'd been missing for five hours, and the weather was stormy. The roads were so bad the Ontario Provincial Police and their tracking dogs hadn't been able to get through. Could Toni and Jiggs help? Toni didn't have to think twice. Of course they could.

Jiggs was a Bouvier des Flandres, a big, rugged dog of a kind originally bred in Europe for herding cattle and general farming tasks. He was a champion in conformation (how well a dog conforms to the physical standards of its breed), obedience and tracking. With the help of a professional trainer, Toni had trained Jiggs as a civil guard dog, with a specialty in search and rescue. Jiggs had learned to search in any kind of terrain and weather; to go through or around any obstacle. He could even sniff out people trapped in collapsed buildings. It took around two and a half years for Jiggs to complete this rigorous training, including a year in the United States for a special course in tracking.

Jiggs started young. When he was not much more than a pup, a German Shepherd escaped from Toni's kennel through a hole in the chain-link fence. Toni decided to see what Jiggs could do. She took him over to the fence and said: "Find him." The next thing she knew, she was flying down the road at the end of Jiggs' nine-metre lead. They crossed three fields, then saw the German Shepherd. The dog plunged into a swamp, and Toni couldn't follow. Every day after that, for three weeks, Jiggs went out on his own looking for the dog, until finally the Shepherd turned up one morning at the back door. "Jiggs lay down with a satisfied air," Toni says, "as if to say, 'Well, I've done it. He came back.'"

Another day, a Doberman named Jet escaped from the kennel. He tore the leash out of Toni's hand and ran away. Jiggs was outside.

"Jet was a male, and of course Jiggs was a male, too, so there could have been problems," Toni says. But Jiggs is a good, peace-loving dog, and Toni knew he wouldn't start a fight. She said: "Go get him!" First, Jiggs ran down to the back of the orchard near the pasture, where the Doberman was heading, and just stood there. Jet swung away from him, heading for the woods. Again, Jiggs ran ahead and blocked the way. "Everywhere that dog went, Jiggs was there before him," says Toni. Finally, Jiggs herded Jet back up the driveway. Toni quickly opened the door of the car and called, "Come on, Jet, let's go for a ride!" The Doberman fell for it and hurled himself into the car.

With such good herding skills, Jiggs' one weakness was not surprising: he liked to chase sheep. "There's something that happens to a dog when it smells a sheep, I think," says Toni. "I had a little lamb that grew up to be a very stupid ewe. She would follow me everywhere, but if she ever started running, I would see an ugly gleam come into Jiggs' eyes. He never took off after her, but he certainly did slobber and drool a lot." Toni laughs. "I think he firmly believed that stupid sheep should be chased!"

> **"That dog searched and that dog searched. He would not quit."**

Jiggs played with Toni's little daughter all the time, but if visitors drove in, he was immediately between them and her until Toni came out and said it was okay.

"If I was ever stiff or unwelcoming, Jiggs made it clear that he wouldn't tolerate the visitor either. It made people pretty uncomfortable when he just stood and stared at them," Toni says. "He was a very large dog."

Despite his size, Jiggs was so well behaved that Toni could take him anywhere. "All of Kemptville knew him," she says. "He was allowed in every store in the town. Everybody loved him. I would go into the bank and say 'Stay,' and he would lie there as long as I wanted him to. One time, a little girl came and sat beside him and started to read him stories. A man came up and greeted her mother, then reached down to ruffle the girl's hair. Jiggs gave him a good growl. 'He won't bite,' I said. 'He's just looking after the child until her mother's done.' He was like that. Very protective."

Jiggs' protectiveness and his calm way with children would be needed, one stormy winter day.

When the call came in, Toni had a moment's doubt. For all Jiggs' training, he had never actually tracked a real person yet. The conditions were so terrible, and the child had been gone so long already — would Jiggs be able to find him? She knew she had to let him try.

The boy had been with a group of children and adults tobogganing on a hill near the woods. Somehow or other, he had wandered off.

"We had a little piece of the boy's clothing," Toni says, "and I gave it to Jiggs to sniff. Then we took him to where they had been tobogganing. Now this is the incredible thing," she goes on. "In the intense cold, the scent does not hold for long, and there were so many tracks around there. I thought, well, this time I can't follow him around on a lead. I've got to let him free. That dog searched and that dog searched, and I had to keep on stopping him to get the snowballs out of his paws. He would not quit. All of a sudden, right near the edge of the woods, he took off and bounded through the trees."

Toni clambered through the bush after him, but then she lost him.

"I thought, I'm going to be lost now," Toni says. "I kept on yelling, 'Jiggs, speak!' the whole time. He would give the odd woof — enough for me to keep track of him."

Toni trailed the dog for an hour and a half. When she finally found him, he was sitting in the middle of tangled undergrowth, with vines wrapped all around him and the little boy hanging onto his neck, snuggled up to him for warmth. Jiggs wouldn't leave the boy, even to come to Toni.

The other searchers caught up to them. Then it took another hour to carry the boy through the deep snow and back out of the woods. The boy's mother was hysterical with relief, but the little boy himself was calm and cheerful. He was much more impressed with "the big dog that came and found me."

"He hadn't really realized the danger he was in," Toni says. "When I found him he just asked, 'Where's Mommy?' I told him she was back with the others, and asked him why he had gone off.

"'I followed the bird,'" he said. 'It was a pretty bird.'"

Jiggs died in 1989. The whole community mourned him. In an obituary printed in the *Kemptville Advance* on the anniversary of his death, he was described as "a champion in the conformation ring, obedience ring and in the tracking field but above all, he was a supreme champion at heart. He gave of himself to the minute he died. He would tackle any task put before him without question and put his life on the line for anyone in his family."

Balloo and Jessie with Ursula Tait

BALLOO AND JESSIE

Berners to the Rescue

Wanda Tait and her daughter, Ursula, flew to Holland to pick up a Bernese Mountain dog named Brigitte. Some years later, Brigitte had her last litter of puppies. Because Brigitte was very special to them, the Taits decided to keep one of these puppies. That was Balloo.

"His personality made itself known very early on in life," Wanda says. "He was always very laid back and independent. The other puppies would all be playing or eating or whatever together, and he would be off doing his own thing — chasing a butterfly, maybe. He was an independent thinker from day one, but he was also a cuddly puppy. He was actually the first dog we ever let sleep on the bed with us. He wasn't so big at first," Wanda says, "but Berners grow. Now, when my husband Eric comes to bed, he has a hard time finding a place for himself!"

Balloo is a champion show dog, but he also knows how to work. Bernese Mountain dogs were originally a Swiss multi-purpose farmer's dog. In particular, they were drovers, dogs who help move cows. They were also used to pull carts. In the summer the farmers would take the sheep and the cows up into the mountains to pasture. The Berners pulled carts with big metal cans full of cream down to the cheese-makers in the valleys. Then they hauled the empty carts back up into the meadows again. Balloo lives up to the tradition by pulling carts and sleds for the Tait family.

"He's our tow rope — like a ski lift," Wanda says. "The girls toboggan down the hill and he pulls the toboggan back up. It's very nice to have him there, because we have a great big, long wooden toboggan that seats six. Everyone loves riding down the hill on it, but it's awful to pull back up. The snow sticks to it. Poor old Balloo gets the job. He doesn't mind at all, though. He's just happy to be there. He takes the girls and the kids in the neighbourhood sledding, too," she adds. "They hitch him up and go for rides all around the place."

The Taits kept one of Balloo's first puppies, too — Jessie. Jessie is a happy dog. She's large for a female, almost as big as Balloo.

"We call her the couch potato," Wanda says. "She doesn't like to be hot, so when she's on the family-room sofa, she stretches out the whole length of it, from end to end, on her back with her tummy up. No one else can sit there."

The Taits live in Rocky Mountain House, Alberta, and love hiking. A friend of theirs made backpacks for the dogs, so whenever they go camping or for picnics, Jessie and Balloo carry their own food as well as some of the family's supplies. In wintertime, when the family goes cross-country skiing, the dogs carry extra gloves and socks.

Whatever the season and whatever the activity, the dogs are pretty useful to have along. But the Taits didn't know how far their usefulness could go until one frightening day.

Fifteen-year-old Ursula Tait was a member of a Search and Rescue program organized by the Royal Canadian Mounted Police. The program teaches basic first aid, and there are also courses in white-water rescue, rope climbing and ice climbing. Ursula and her best friend Nina Hofer had been part of it for over a year and had been on quite a few search-and-rescue missions. On one of them, they found an animal trail that led along a steep hill to a beautiful, wild sort of place. They wanted to go back to it, and when they did, a few weeks later, they took Balloo and Jessie with them.

> **"They were so protective — at first, Jessie wouldn't let anyone near me."**

"As we walked up the trail," Ursula says, "I had a headache. I had taken some Tylenol, and I got dizzy. I don't know exactly what happened, but I fell."

Ursula plunged about fifty metres down the hill-side. To Nina's horror, she was headed straight for rocks and a tree. Balloo lunged after her. He got beneath her and used his body to stop her fall.

Nina worked her way down the hill to Ursula as

quickly as she could, with Jessie following. Ursula was unconscious. She was bleeding from cuts on her head, back and legs. When she regained consciousness, after about five minutes, she was able to talk to Nina, saying her back hurt. Both girls knew the dangers of moving a person with a back injury, so they decided Ursula had better stay as still as possible and they would wait for a rescue party to find them.

"We weren't scared," Ursula says. With all their rescue and survival training, the girls knew just what to do. Nina built a fire and covered Ursula with extra clothes and blankets from their backpacks. Balloo had not moved from where he had thrown himself to stop Ursula's fall. Now, both dogs curled up as close to the injured girl as possible, Balloo at her side and Jessie at her head.

The temperature dropped to three degrees Celsius that night. "The dogs kept me warm the most," Ursula says, "I mean, the whole night we were shivering, but without the dogs, it would have been a lot worse. It rained off and on and it was really cold." Nina had to keep moving Jessie, who was tucked in so close to Ursula's face that the girl could hardly breathe.

The two girls heard coyotes or wolves howling all through the long hours of darkness, but they knew the dogs would keep off any animals that came prowling during the night. (In fact, the next day they did find fresh bear tracks around their campsite.) Early the next morning, just at the break of dawn, Ursula and Nina heard a rescue team calling out to each other on their radios. They heard someone say that they could see a fire. The girls knew it must be theirs.

Nina blew long and hard on her whistle and then yelled. A yell came back. Within minutes, one of the searchers came running up the hill.

"The dogs went wild," Ursula says, "but they were so protective — at first, Jessie wouldn't let anyone near me."

The area was too isolated and the bush too dense to get an ambulance in, so a helicopter flew Ursula out, immobilized on a flatboard. Luckily, she was only in the hospital for a day, and there was no serious injury to her back.

Balloo and Jessie were both inducted into the Ralston Purina Hall of Fame for their heroic actions. Only Balloo was able to go, however, as Jessie was expecting pups. He flew to Toronto with the Taits to receive the awards. And he revelled in all the attention that came with them.

Grizzly with his team

GRIZZLY

The Dog Who Fought a Bear

It was about ten o'clock on a warm June morning when Paul Guitard decided to take his sled dogs for a run. As usual in the summer months, he harnessed his team up to his four-wheel all-terrain vehicle. His lead dog was a black and silver-grey purebred Siberian Husky named Grizzly.

A few years before, Paul had bought a Siberian Husky named Kiska, just because he liked the looks of the breed. After he got her he went to a sled dog race and thought it looked like fun. He became more and more interested, and finally decided to buy a male, build up his own team, and see what he could do.

Grizzly was the male Paul chose, and soon Kiska had puppies. "I kept a bunch and started hooking them up to a sled, and first thing you know, I got hooked!" Paul says.

Over the years, Grizzly helped Paul train the young dogs, and eventually one of them took over as lead dog of Paul's racing team. But even the fastest dog can't replace Grizzly in the hearts of Paul and his family. For loyal, steadfast Grizzly is more than a sled dog — he's a hero.

On that warm June morning, with Grizzly in the lead, the dogs were running well. They were about three kilometres down the trail when suddenly, out of nowhere, a black bear charged out of the bush. Before Paul had time to realize what was happening, the bear was on top of him and savagely biting his leg and arm.

"I looked over and saw two cubs on the path — we'd come between them and their mother — and I thought, Uh, oh. I'm in trouble! Then, all of a sudden, the bear pulled me right off my bike. The dogs went on a hundred metres or so and I thought they were gone."

Normally, if Paul falls off or loses the team, the dogs just keep right on going. But Grizzly knew Paul was in trouble. He brought the team to a halt, turned them all and the bike and headed back to Paul. In harness and still attached to the rest of the team, Grizzly went for the bear. The bear released Paul and turned to fight the dog; Paul scrambled for the nearest tree. As he started up it, the bear's jaws closed on his right foot.

"I was kicking her with my other foot, trying to make her let me go, and she was pulling me back down the tree," Paul recalls. "Then Grizzly went at her again and started biting at her, so she let me go. I climbed up to the top of the tree fast!"

Grizzly stationed himself at the bottom of the tree, between Paul and the bear. The cubs ran to the other side of the trail and up a tree of their own.

"I expected that when everything calmed down everybody would leave," Paul says. The cubs left after about two hours, but their mother stayed. Every twenty minutes or so she made another rush for the tree, and each time Grizzly fought her off. When he charged, the harness pulled all the other dogs forward too, but they weren't about to help fight a bear. In fact, just to add to Grizzly's problems, they began to fight among themselves — until Grizzly sorted them out.

The day became hotter. Paul sat in the tree, sweating, knowing he was going to be there for a while, until someone missed him and started trying to find him. His right arm and leg were bleeding badly, and he was in a lot of pain.

"I just sat up there and waited," he says, "and every time the bear charged the tree I wondered, is she going to get up this time?"

But Grizzly kept her away. After three or four hours, the bear ambled about 200 metres off and settled herself down to sleep. Paul began to think about sneaking down the tree, unhooking the dogs, and getting away on the bike. Cautiously, he began to climb down.

> "I looked over and saw two cubs on the path — we'd come between them and their mother."

"I got about halfway down. She put her head up, looked at me, and gave a kind of a grunt. She started to get up. 'Hey, no problem!' I said, and headed back up my tree."

About an hour after that — six hours since the bear attacked — Paul finally heard more all-terrain vehicles coming. He knew it was probably his brother-in-law and friend coming to look for him. Paul screamed at them to go home and get a gun, so they turned around.

"That was the toughest time," Paul says now, "because I was so close to getting saved, and if she got up there before they got back . . ." He broke a branch off the tree and made a little spear out of it — anything to keep the bear away if she did get up. But Grizzly remained on guard, and the bear didn't get through.

At last Paul heard his friends returning. The bear heard them too. She crossed over to the other side of the trail and waited for them. Just as they came into sight, she charged. She was only a few metres away when Paul's friend shot her. Paul stayed where he was long enough to make sure the bear was really dead; then, fighting pain and fatigue, he clambered down the tree.

The first thing he did was tend to Grizzly. The dog had only a small gash on his nose where one of the bear's claws had caught him. In spite of being hampered by the harness and all the other dogs, he had still managed to be faster on his feet than the lumbering bear.

Paul, however, had a gash on his right arm and the calf of his right leg was cut open. And he found out later that he had broken his left ankle from kicking the bear in the nose.

"Not that it did much good," he says now. "I

think it only made her madder. It was Grizzly who saved me. I can honestly say, and I've said it a hundred times, I wouldn't be here if it weren't for that dog. I'd be dead. That bear would have killed me."

When he got home and had had his wounds tended to, Paul worried about the cubs whose mother had been shot. An animal biologist who called to talk to him about it later on assured him that the cubs were probably old enough to take care of themselves by then. He also said that the bear's behaviour in not going after her cubs once they had left was so unusual that there must have been something wrong.

Grizzly is older now, and has slowed down a little. But he still races with Paul's son. He has a privileged place among all the other dogs. When Paul is away, his wife Jan brings Grizzly into the house for company. The dog who faced down a bear loves being a family pet; he'll happily let the children pull his ears and maul him to their hearts' content.

"He's just a happy-go-lucky, never-does-anything-wrong dog," Paul says, his voice full of affection and pride.

Racing Sled Dogs

The best racing sled dogs are Alaskan Huskies, a mix of purebred Siberian Huskies and Border Collies or hounds such as Salukis or Greyhounds. The Husky part gives these dogs their toughness and ability to withstand the cold, the hound or Border Collie part gives them their speed.

Although this is not a registered breed, each dog has a pedigree of its own. Every one of the eleven dogs in a team is scrupulously cared for. When racing on icy snow and rough tracks, they wear specially fitted boots.

Racing dogs are not pets. They live in a kennel. They snarl and growl and fight among themselves. But with people they are loving, gentle dogs. When Paul Guitard's young children are in the kennel with him they're in and out of the doghouses, playing with them all the time.

"These sled dogs," Paul says, "the only way they're going to hurt you is if they lick you to death."

FEATHERED FRIEND

When an alligator invaded Gail and Howard Ennis's Florida home, Gail was awakened just in time by the squawking of Louie, their 11-year-old African Grey parrot. The Ennises say that Louie, captured in the wild when very young, acted on instinct because he recognized a predator.

Bruno with Donnie Skiffington

BRUNO

A Boy's Best Friend

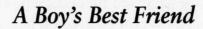

It was a hot sunny day in August. The Skiffington family was enjoying the weather at their cabin in Lethbridge, on the eastern coast of Newfoundland. The cabin is on a bay, and so close to the water the family can watch whales swim past.

Eleven-year-old Donnie wanted to go swimming, but his parents were busy and there was no one to go with him. He decided to go for a bike ride instead. Of course his dog, Bruno, went with him. Bruno is the family's German Shepherd and Donnie's best friend and protector. Donnie and his brother Jeffrey had given Bruno to their mother, Cindy, for Christmas, and from the very first he was a playful and loyal pet. He quickly became the boys' guardian. When he was only eight months old, a moose came into the garden where the boys were playing, and Bruno chased it out. "Chased it out of the garden and clear across the road," Cindy Skiffington says.

Bruno is best friends with the family cat as well. Cindy was a little worried about how he would react

113

when the little kitten arrived. But he took to her right away. "It was just a little kitten, but a feisty one," Cindy says. "She took to Bruno, too, and they play together and sleep together. Sometimes Bruno leans down and sort of paws at her to get her attention. Then, when he's asleep, she'll go over and nip on his ear. Some nights we'll see them asleep, and he'll have his two huge paws wrapped around her. He's so huge, and she's so tiny. He'll take her right in his mouth, but he'd never nip her, and she's never had any fear of him. They even eat out of the same dish.

"Some people think dogs are stunned," Cindy goes on. "They think they're just dumb animals, but they're not." She gives an example of just how understanding a dog can be. One winter, when they were in the woods trying to get a really heavy log out, Eric, Donnie's father, turned to the dog.

"Bruno, grab hold of the rope now and give me a hand, hauling this log," he said. He didn't really think the dog would do it, but Bruno trotted right up, grabbed the rope in his teeth and pulled. Together, they got the log out.

On this particular day in August, Donnie decided to bike over to see a friend who lived nearby. On the way was a steep hill, and Donnie went down it fast. The grass was still wet and slippery from the morning mist, and when he tried to brake, the bike skidded and struck a rock. Donnie was thrown off. The bike hit him in the face, then Donnie careered on down the hill. Catapulted into a ditch at the bottom, he was knocked unconscious. He lay still, bleeding.

Bruno raced back up the hill to get help. He found Cindy first, but when he bounced and barked at her, she just thought he wanted to play.

"Goon," she said, "I haven't got time for you today."

Then Bruno went on over to Eric, who was up on the hill sawing wood. Eric didn't pay any attention to him either, so Bruno bolted back to Donnie. He grabbed the collar of Donnie's shirt, and began to drag him out of the ditch and back up to the cabin.

> **"Some nights we'll see them asleep, and he'll have his two huge paws wrapped around her."**

At this point, Donnie began to regain consciousness.

All he can remember now is something wet and slobbery pulling him along. He started to cry. Eric and Cindy heard him crying, and ran to help. When they reached him, they could see that Donnie's face was covered with blood. There was a big gash on his forehead, and his eye seemed to be bleeding as well. Luckily for Donnie, although he had to have sixteen stitches in his forehead and four in his eyelid, his sight was not affected at all.

Friends who stayed at the cabin while the Skiffingtons were at the hospital said that Bruno never left the doorstep. He just sat there, watching and waiting for Donnie's return. When he finally heard the van, he got excited. He rushed to meet

Donnie, then followed him as Donnie's parents helped him back into the house and onto the couch. Bruno stationed himself beside the couch, and wouldn't move as long as Donnie was there. In all the days following, while Donnie recovered, Bruno refused to leave his side.

Bruno was given the Ralston Purina Award. He and the Skiffington family were picked up at the airport in a special limousine, and they were given two days they won't ever forget. Bruno had his own doggy sitter while the Skiffingtons toured Toronto.

On the way home, there was a mixup in the flight schedules, and Bruno ended up waiting for the rest of the family at the St. John's airport for several hours. It didn't bother him a bit. In fact, he seemed to enjoy all the attention he got from people coming up to his cage, where he lay waiting.

"They talked to him and gave him water," Cindy says. When the family finally caught up to him, he was having a great time. "He's a wonderful dog." That's what the Skiffingtons say, and they mean it.

HALL OF FAME

Each year, the Ralston Purina Hall of Fame inducts animals who have performed outstanding acts of courage, intelligence and loyalty.

In the 32 years since the Hall of Fame began, 104 animals have been inducted — 83 dogs, 17 cats and 1 horse.

Max and Dolly with Vera Soudek

MAX

The Protector

Max the Bouvier and Dolly the Dachshund are the best of friends. Sometimes they get into trouble, and it's usually Dolly who gets them into it. But Max is the one who gets them out.

Dachshunds are hunters. They were originally trained to burrow into the dens of badgers and foxes. Once underground, they could not hear commands, so they had to be able to make their own decisions. Independent thinking was the character trait a dachshund's master prized most, and that trait has survived in the breed to this day.

When Vera Soudek got Dolly, the dog was so tiny Vera could hold her in one hand. She was a sweet little dog, but 100 percent dachshund.

"For example," Vera says, "I would say, 'Down.' Dolly would sit and then look at me as if to say, 'This is good enough, isn't it?' Or when I said, 'Give me a paw,' she would roll over, then later on she would suddenly come over and give me her paw, all on her own. But she's very brave, and not scared of anything."

When Dolly was a year old, Vera got Max. Vera had always wanted a Bouvier des Flandres. Bouviers are very big dogs, however: as a puppy, Max was already as big as Dolly. So Vera was a little concerned. But she needn't have worried. When Max saw Dolly for the first time in the backyard, he yelped and ran away. Dolly had never seen a dog like Max, but she wasn't the least bit scared. In fact, she decided to become his mother. While Max was young, if any other dog attacked him, she defended him — even though she was smaller than he was!

Now that he is full-grown, Max has become the family protector. Vera remembers one day when she took him out in the car. It was a hot day, and the window was down. Max was lying on the floor of the front seat, out of sight of anyone outside the car. Vera stopped at a red light. Suddenly, she saw a hand reach through the window of the passenger side and pull up the lock button. Max sat up, and his great head rose into view. The hand disappeared as quickly as it had appeared. Vera never even had time to glimpse the person it was attached to.

And, one day, Max came to the rescue when Dolly's instinct for hunting got her into trouble.

That day, Vera decided to take the two dogs for a walk on Bell's Island, on the Cataraqui River. "It's a beautiful place," Vera says, "full of big old trees." And it was a lovely, early November day. There had been a few cold nights already, and there was a thin layer of ice on the river. It was sunny, and the trees were golden. There was no one else around, so Vera let the dogs run loose. They ran ahead of her, out of sight, and she was just about to whistle them back, when suddenly a volley of barking broke out. Mixed in with the barking was another sound — a strange noise Vera couldn't identify.

Vera started to go after the dogs, then realized that the ground was becoming very marshy. Carefully, she made her way by stepping from one clump of vegetation to another. Meanwhile, the barking and the other strange noise were getting more and more ferocious. Finally, she came to where Dolly and Max were, at the river's edge. There was a terrible commotion going on in the water. Vera saw that the dogs were fighting a raccoon. Dolly's hunting instinct had led her to tackle something much too fierce, even for her.

As Vera watched in horror, the raccoon grabbed Dolly by the ear and dove under the water, dragging Dolly down. Vera knew that this was a raccoon's favourite way of fighting, as it can stay underwater much longer than a dog can.

"I didn't know what to do," Vera recalls. The water was deep, and the bottom was covered with thick mud. The river current was strong, too, and there was a good chance Vera would get swept in if she tried to wade in and help. But, if the raccoon held Dolly down much longer, the little dog would drown.

The rear end of the raccoon was still above water. Max saw his chance and took it. He locked his jaws around the raccoon's back and shook. Finally, the raccoon let Dolly go. She surfaced, covered in mud, with blood streaming down her ears. It had been enough for her. She splashed out of the water and streaked for the car, parked about two kilometres away.

"I hated to leave Max," Vera said, "but I thought, he's a big strong dog, he can handle a raccoon. So I went after Dolly."

Max followed her in a very short time.

"I don't know whether he killed the raccoon or not," Vera says. "It seemed to be tired out. I think it probably just gave up and ran away." But not before biting Max viciously on the legs.

Vera took both dogs to the veterinarian. Dolly's ears healed up nicely, but Max's legs got badly infected. His front legs were so badly injured that, for a while, they were afraid he would never walk again. He did heal, but he was bandaged for weeks. "He was a good patient," Vera says.

Dolly and Max have their breakfast together every morning now. Dolly likes to be wrapped in her blanket and then cuddle back into bed with Vera. Max rather likes being in the bed, too, but he gets too warm and has to get down onto the tiles to cool off. They're still the best of friends, and so far, since their fearful raccoon encounter, they've managed to stay out of trouble.

UGLY SISTER

The *Ottawa Citizen* reprinted a short article from China's *Sichuan Daily* newspaper. It told of a cat named Ugly Sister, who saved her master, his wife and their five children. She woke them late one night by meowing, scratching, and even pulling on the trouser legs of her owner, alerting them to the fact that the walls of their two-storey mud house were crumbling. The family escaped just minutes before the building collapsed, and no one was hurt.

Perhaps the family changed their cat's name afterward, in gratitude to their rescuer.

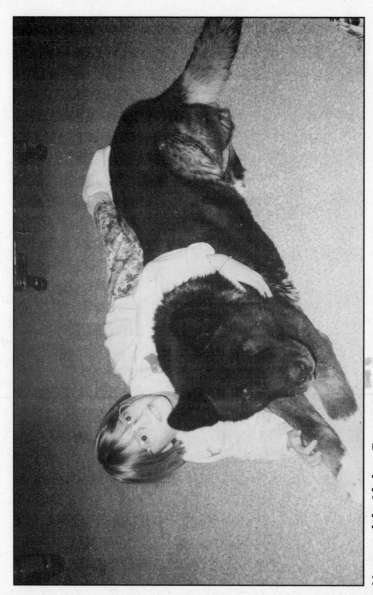

Nago with Alaina Fawcett

NAGO

The Dog Babysitter

Jeff and Loys Fawcett got their Akita, Nago, when he was seven weeks old. As a puppy he was the centre of attention in their household — almost like a first child. So when the Fawcetts had their first baby, they were a little worried. But Nago wasn't jealous at all. He licked the baby on the back of the head until she was soaking wet, and from that moment on, Lynn and then her sisters Alaina and Elizabeth were Nago's special charges.

"If anyone comes into the yard when the girls are playing outside, Nago just puts himself between the person and the children and won't let them near him," Loys says. "He doesn't growl — just stands there and looks mean."

Nago is a fierce guard dog when he thinks it's necessary, and not only with the children. When the family is out, he's often tied outside. A man working on the house one day came up and offered him half a sandwich. Nago took it, then dropped it on the ground. He wouldn't eat it. The man persisted, and put his hand out to touch Nago. Luckily he was wearing thick gloves. Nago discouraged him with a bite that wasn't quite hard enough to break through the glove, but hard enough to let the man know he was on duty and didn't like strangers around, even if they brought sandwiches. Two hours later when Loys came home, the sandwich was still lying untouched on the ground, and the workman was keeping his distance.

And one night, a man approached Loys when she was walking Nago. She still isn't sure what the man's intentions were, but he never had a chance to make them clear. Before he could get near her, Nago snarled, snapped, and lunged for him. The dog was on the lead and it took all of her strength for Loys to hold him back.

But for all his fierceness, Nago is a quiet dog, and well aware of his own size. Normally, he's careful not to bump or push too hard against anyone, especially the children. He is so friendly and gentle that he is a favourite visitor at schools where Loys takes him to teach children dog manners — what they should or shouldn't do around dogs. He visits hospitals, where patients love to pat him. He snuffles up to touch noses, making friends immediately. At one hospital there was an elderly man who wouldn't respond to anyone, just sat for hours in his wheelchair, staring at nothing, his hands clasped in his lap. When Loys brought Nago into that ward, the first person Nago went up to was that man. He stuck his nose into the man's stomach and laid his head on his lap. The old man's face lit up and he started fondling the dog's ears. It turned out he was a farmer who had had a big dog of his own before he'd become ill, and Nago must have triggered memories of his own pet.

Gentle or not, Nago has a lot of energy. To run some of it off, Loys and Jeff will often take him out and let him run behind the car on the country roads near where they live. Thirty kilometres an hour is just fine for him, even at ten years old. Because of this more-than-usual need for exercise, Loys lets him run loose whenever possible.

Nago was loose one cold March morning when Loys, Lynn, Alaina and Elizabeth set out for the stop sign at the top of the hill to wait for the school bus. It looked like it was going to be a warm day, just like the day before, though there had been a freeze overnight and it was still icy underfoot. Nago bounded along in the fields beside the girls. When they got to the road, Loys called Nago to heel and commanded him to sit beside her. Six-year-old Alaina started to play in the dirt beside the stop sign; the other two girls were with Loys.

> She was going to scold Nago when Lynn shouted: "Alaina was just about hit!"

"Nago doesn't break a command," Loys says, "but he will put variations on it. He'll obey, but it's got to be on his terms." Today Nago sat obediently when she told him to, but faced the opposite way from Loys, who was watching for the bus.

So, Nago was the only one who saw the truck

coming up the hill toward them, towing a manure spreader. Only Nago saw the truck hit an icy patch and skid out of control. Only Nago saw the huge manure spreader jackknife, and head straight for Alaina.

Nago hurled himself at Alaina, nearly knocking her off her feet. She grabbed for a handful of his fur in order to keep from being bowled over, and found herself being dragged away from the road. "You dumb dog!" she cried.

All this happened in just seconds. "Nago and Alaina suddenly appeared in front of me and I realized he'd broken my command," Loys says. She was going to scold Nago when Lynn shouted: "Alaina was just about hit!"

Loys whirled around. The manure spreader was inches away from the stop sign where Alaina had been playing moments before. The truck driver was sitting in shock, his head down on his hands on the steering wheel. Loys and Lynn dove for Nago.

"Good dog!" they cried.

"What's so good about him stepping on me?" Alaina complained.

Today, Loys shakes her head. "I don't know whether animals actually think things out or not," she says, "but I do know that Nago never breaks a command, and when he saw that truck coming for Alaina, he saved her."

The Akita

Akitas were bred for hunting bear, deer and wild boar in the rugged mountains of northern Japan. At one time only the royal family and other rulers of Japan were allowed to own Akitas. Now this breed has become so widely known and beloved in its home country that the Japanese government designated the dog a national monument and treasure. To the Japanese, the Akita is a symbol of good health. Small Akita statues are given as get-well gifts to sick people, or to newborn babies as a wish for long life, health and happiness.

The Akita is a big, heavy-set, muscular dog, with upstanding ears, a sturdy body with a short, thick coat, and a tail that curls luxuriously over its back. It can be white or tawny brown, with dark streaks or patches. Tawny and spotted dogs have dark masks or blazes on their faces.

Akitas are affectionate and loyal with family and friends, and fierce in defending them against strangers. In times past, Japanese mothers would even leave their children to the care of these dogs.

Wrinkles with Floyd and Lila Lockyer

WRINKLES

The Brave Little Dachshund

On their way home from Florida, Floyd and Lila Lockyer stopped overnight at a motel. Early the next morning, they were packing up the car to leave. Floyd went back into the room to get the last bags, telling Lila she could bring Wrinkles, their nine-year-old Dachshund, out to the car. As he went to close the motel-room door, two men started to push their way in. Alarmed, Floyd tried to shut the door on them, but one of them stuck his foot in the opening and then forced his way in. He had a gun. Lila turned around and saw him, and as she did, the intruder pointed the gun at her and Wrinkles.

Wrinkles hadn't been feeling too perky that morning and he was still lying on the bed, but as soon as he saw the intruder, he leaped up. He jumped off the bed and attacked the man. Small as he was, Wrinkles got him by the leg and didn't let go. The man pointed the gun down at Wrinkles and fired. Luckily, the shot missed. At the same time, Lila rushed forward to help Wrinkles, but tripped and hit her head on the door frame.

With Wrinkles hanging on to his ankle in determination, the gunman decided he'd had enough. Trying to shake the dog off his leg, he backed up and out the door. Floyd managed to pull Wrinkles off and slam the door shut.

"The second guy was right behind the first one," Floyd says. "He didn't get a chance to do anything because the first one backed up when Wrinkles got hold of him. Without the dog, there was no way we could have protected ourselves."

Lila was bleeding quite badly from a gash on her forehead. Floyd called 9-1-1, and help was there almost immediately. After spending several hours in the hospital, Lila was released, and the family was able to go on home the next day.

Floyd and Lila got Wrinkles when he was a four-month-old pup.

"He's very protective of us," Floyd says. "Dachshunds are protective little fellows. But he's a very loving dog. If I'm in the living room, sitting in a chair, he wants to get up on my knee. He's certainly our hero and a good companion."

As the Lockyers found out after they got home, the reason Wrinkles hadn't been feeling well that morning was that he had developed diabetes. The veterinarian told them that they could either treat him or put him down.

"We thought, how could we put a dog down that had just saved our lives?" Floyd recalls, so they started treatment. The dog had to go into the animal hospital for a while until they got him on insulin and got the diabetes under control. Wrinkles is home now, and Lila gives him an insulin shot in the morning and at night.

Unfortunately, because of the disease and his age — he's twelve years old — he has become blind. But he still gets around fine.

> **"Dachshunds are protective little fellows."**

"He's got his favourite little places in the house where he lies," Floyd says. "He can get around real well." He gets a little shaky sometimes, and a bit disoriented, but he still goes out for walks when the Lockyers go back to Florida.

"He likes that," Floyd says. "You have to be his guide dog when you go out for a walk. But he's spunky. When somebody comes to the door, he sure lets us know they're there."

Wrinkles received the Ralston Purina Award for his bravery. Part of the award was a supply of dog food, which he couldn't eat because he is on a special diet. So the Lockyers donated it to an animal shelter where they live.

BUNNY ON ALERT

Downy, a 3-year-old white bunny, is credited with saving the lives of 11 people when a fire broke out in an apartment building in Wisbech, England. Awakened by the smoke and flames, Downy went into his owner's room, stood on his hind legs and clawed at her bedside table until she woke up.

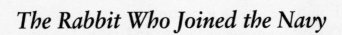

The Rabbit Who Joined the Navy

When the Second World War broke out, Jock McGregor was living in the United States. He was a British subject and wanted to fight for his country, but he couldn't get back to England. He came to Canada instead, and joined the Royal Canadian Navy.

"It was a very very fortunate thing for me," he says. "I made many good friends and I'll always treasure this decision."

After a few years he was drafted to the *Haida*, a Canadian destroyer that, in 1944, was making nightly trips into the English channel to search for German submarines and do battle. During Jock's tour of duty the ship had many mascots, but there is one he remembers most fondly.

One night after some of the ship's crew had been on shore leave in Plymouth, they came back aboard with a baby rabbit. They put it on Jock's gun platform. In the morning, when he went to clean his guns and get them ready for action, there was the little rabbit, about eight centimetres long, sitting up and begging like a dog.

Jock went ashore and asked for help from the Wrens, the women's branch of the Royal Navy. They managed to find some dandelion leaves, and together they and Jock filled a whole bag full — enough to last a rabbit at sea for a long time.

The rabbit grew and grew and grew. The ship's doctor warned Jock that rabbits have very sensitive hearing. If the ship went into action, the shock of the gun noise would probably kill it. He advised Jock to get rid of the rabbit, but Jock couldn't bear to part with it.

The ship did see action. The rabbit not only survived, but became a pet of the whole ship. Then one night one of the stokers came up carrying a bin full of potatoes. The rabbit, which was tame by this time, heard the footsteps and hopped over, probably hoping it was Jock coming with more dandelion greens. The stoker didn't see the small animal and slammed the potato locker down on its leg. The leg was broken.

Jock took the rabbit to the ship's doctor. At first the doctor thought it should just be put out of its misery, but Jock persuaded him to splint the leg. The doctor did so, with two tiny pieces of wood and some plaster of paris.

"It hopped about like a little wounded sailor," Jock says.

About the fourth day the rabbit started to chew on the plaster until it fell off. Jock found that the leg had healed well and the rabbit was fine, although still limping.

The ship's doctor had been right about one thing, however. The rabbit did have very sensitive hearing —

and a unusual talent. Normally quiet and peaceful, from time to time the rabbit would suddenly begin to squeak and hop about. Though puzzled at first by the rabbit's agitation, the crew of the *Haida* soon learned what it meant: the enemy was approaching. Forewarned, they prepared for battle. The crew grew quite confident about the rabbit's mysterious forecasting abilities.

After some time at sea the *Haida* sank a German submarine. Jock was the one who saw it surfacing and opened fire. The news of the victory was reported in the newspapers back in England, along with the story of the rabbit. The Duchess of Kent wrote a letter to Jock, asking if his rabbit could join the mascot club of the United Kingdom because it had survived all the action the *Haida* had seen. Jock filled out the application she sent, as did Captain Harry de Wolfe. The rabbit signed with its paw, pressed in a pad of ink and stamped on the application.

The Duchess of Kent sent Jock a grateful letter and a medal for the rabbit. The medal was for fidelity, which means faithfulness. Jock believes this is the only rabbit in the world to hold such an honour.

After the war, the rabbit lived peacefully in Halifax with Captain de Wolfe. The *Haida* is now permanently moored at the Toronto waterfront, and is open to visitors who would like to see the ship — the home, for a while, of a brave little rabbit.

Tia

TIA

The Labrador Who Retrieved a Boat

It was a cold, windy day. Heavy rain was falling. Sean Lingl and his friend Danny Parker were beginning to think their decision to go duck hunting was a mistake. Sitting between them, unmindful of the awful weather and eager to get to work, was Sean's chocolate Labrador Retriever, Tia.

They were paddling a small dinghy to an island in the mouth of the Nimpkish River, off northern Vancouver Island. The wind coming in against the current was whipping the water up into bigger and bigger waves. With the rain and the waves crashing over the bow, water was lapping around their feet and getting deeper by the minute.

The boat rocked alarmingly; paddling was getting more and more difficult. The dinghy was constructed with two layers of plastic hull. The air trapped between the layers was supposed to make the boat unsinkable. Unknown to Sean, however, there was a hole in the outermost layer, and the boat was taking on water. Suddenly, the dinghy heeled over to one side.

"We're in trouble," Sean yelled to Danny. "We'd better get back to shore."

They tried to turn the boat around, but the wind caught it. Instantly, it turned upside-down.

Sean found himself in the freezing water, clinging to the side of the overturned dinghy. Beside him, his friend Danny also clung to the boat. Tia was nowhere to be seen.

She must be trapped under the boat, Sean thought, and groped desperately for her. He found her and pulled her out. He let her go, thinking she would swim to shore.

After rescuing Tia, Sean turned his mind to his own problem. Both he and Danny were wearing chest-high hip waders. Sean was worried. He had heard stories of people being dragged down as their waders filled with water, and of trapped air in the high boots causing the wearer to flip upside-down.

And they were in the Pacific Ocean in the middle of winter. The water was frigid. If they didn't get out right away, the cold would kill them.

Suddenly, Sean realized that the boat was moving through the water. He looked ahead and saw Tia, the mooring line clenched firmly between her teeth, swimming strongly toward the shore. As soon as they realized what she was doing, Sean and Danny began to help as much as they could by kicking their feet.

They were about a hundred metres away from Vancouver Island, and the water was wild. But Tia ploughed steadily on. The two men's feet finally touched bottom and they staggered on shore.

Once on land, the wind cut through their soaked

clothing. Now they were really cold. They ran the short distance to the truck, Tia romping at their heels. The men may have been suffering, but Labradors like nothing better than ice-cold water, and Tia was not at all the worse for her dip. Sean and Danny, however, were glad it was only a fifteen-minute drive home and to warm, dry clothes.

What Tia had done was so incredible that at first Sean was reluctant to tell anybody other than his wife, Marnie, about it. You see, Tia has only three legs.

Sean got Tia as a pup. Labrador Retrievers are dogs with immense amounts of energy, and they need a lot of exercise. Sean was in the habit of running her regularly. One day, there was a ditch filled with water beside the road they were on. If Labs see water, they have to be in it. It seems to be an unwritten rule. So of course Tia plunged joyfully into the ditch and ran through it. Unfortunately, someone must have thrown a bottle in there and it had broken. Tia yelped, and came out bleeding. Sean looked her over and found that she had cut the pad of her right back paw very badly.

> "We're in trouble. We'd better get back to shore."

Sean took her to his veterinarian, but because the cut was right through the pad, the vet was unable to stitch it. He bandaged it, and they tried to keep Tia off her feet. But in spite of their care, the foot became infected and the infection spread up into the leg. They sent Tia to an animal hospital in Campbell River. There, the doctors tried for three days to save her leg, but finally notified Sean that it would have to be amputated.

"We thought about getting her put to sleep," Sean says. "I didn't want to see her not able to move."

But the vet told him that chances were Tia would be able to get around fine with only three legs. "Actually, it often takes the owner longer to get used to it than the dog," he said.

Sean didn't want to lose Tia, so he agreed to the operation.

"She was grabbing sticks and wanting to run the first day we had her home," Sean says now. "We had to slow her down. She adapted right away. It was just like she never even knew it was gone."

Tia can run just about as fast as ever, and jump over anything in her path. The only time she has a bit of trouble is climbing hills or scrambling through rocky places. She went right back to her job of retrieving ducks for Sean when they went hunting, jumping out of the boat with no trouble at all. And fetching balls remains her favourite game. She never gets tired.

"When you're finished playing with her, she'll just want to keep on," Sean says. "She'll follow you around with that ball and then drop it on the ground in front of you and push with her nose until it rolls on your feet."

Like most Labs, Tia is also great with children. Sean's wife, Marnie, is from a big family, so in addition to their own two daughters, there are often eight or nine nieces and nephews around. Tia is often literally covered with children crawling all over her, pulling on her hair and her whiskers. She just lies there and loves it. She'll play rough with Sean, but when it comes to the children she's always gentle.

Tia was awarded the Ralston Purina Animal Hall of Fame Award for her intelligence and bravery, and thoroughly enjoyed the trip to Toronto with Sean and Marnie to receive it. VIP treatment at a big hotel, a special doggy sitter, and travelling by limousine everywhere she went suited her just fine.

And Sean Lingl and Danny Parker believe she deserved every bit of it.

Shana with the Laurins

SHANA

The Dog Who Conquered Her Own Greatest Fear

Shana was an intelligent, loving, even-tempered dog, typical of the Newfoundland in every way but one: she was afraid of the water.

Dorothy Laurin got Shana from a breeder in Pincher Creek, Alberta, when the pup was about seven weeks old. When Shana was nine months old, she made the mistake of leaning too far over the edge of a dock and fell in. It was her first experience with water. The pup panicked as the water closed over her head and she nearly drowned. By the time she figured out how to swim and got back to shore, she had decided that, Newfoundland or not, deep water was not for her.

Shana came from seven generations of champion show dogs, but Dorothy did not want to put her into the show ring. Instead, Shana became a beloved family pet. She absolutely adored children. On her walks through the city she would pass by every adult or dog she met without slowing down, but the minute she saw a child she'd get excited and want to play. She liked nothing better than to be harnessed up to Dorothy's son Kevin's wagon to give children rides. She would even help him deliver his newspapers on his newspaper route. Dorothy recalls the time Kevin had over two hundred papers to deliver and asked his sister, Michele, to help him.

"I don't know your route," Michele protested.

"Shana does," Kevin answered.

So while he did one side of the road, Michele did the other with Shana. The big, black-haired dog pulled the wagon and stopped at every house that took the paper. She knew the route, all right!

Shana was never one for playing with a ball, but she did love fluffy slippers. Every Christmas she received a new pair as a present. No — she didn't wear them! She would sit on the floor, slipper in her mouth, and Kevin would grasp the other end for a lively game of tug-of-war. With all the strength Shana had in her powerful muscles, she'd pull him right across the floor. She was also best friends with the family cat; they could often be found curled up sleeping together.

Grooming Shana was sometimes a bit of a challenge. Although she liked it once the brushing actually started, she would worry at the first sight of the brush and comb. Dorothy remembers one time when her husband, Herman, got out the grooming equipment and Shana took a flying leap onto the couch, trying — unsuccessfully — to hide her fifty-five-kilogram bulk behind poor Kevin.

Shana loved it out in the bush, and had her own tent for camping with the family. She never got as far as swimming at a beach, but she did have her own private pool. Dorothy and Herman bought her a children's wading pool to cool off in during the summer heat. It was shallow, and only just big enough for her to lie down in, so she didn't find it threatening. In fact, on hot summer nights Shana would often want to go out, and as Dorothy and Herman waited impatiently to let her back in, they would hear water splashing. Shana was having a midnight dip.

Then came the freak storm that hit Calgary, Alberta, on August 16, 1988. Dorothy and Herman were sitting outside their house that evening, talking to their neighbour and watching him cut his lawn. It was peaceful and warm — they had no hint at all of what was about to occur. The neighbour happened to look up at the sky at seven o'clock.

"I'd better hurry up," he said. "Looks like it's going to rain." The clouds were black and coming up fast. Dorothy and Herman went inside.

A heavy rain began, and within minutes it was pelting down. Then came the hail. The water rose as first streets, then lawns became flooded. There was a crash from below and the sound of breaking glass. Dorothy and Herman rushed downstairs to find that a basement window had caved in with the pressure and the house was starting to fill with water. Dorothy headed for the front door, closely followed by her husband, but the moment she opened it, she found herself engulfed and carried away in a torrent of rushing water. The street had been transformed into a raging, ice-filled river.

"There was nothing to hold on to," Dorothy says.

"I was really struggling. If I had gone under I would not have been able to get out."

She screamed for help, but before her husband could do anything, Shana, the dog who was deathly afraid of deep water, dove in. Without the slightest hesitation she swam toward her floundering owner. Dorothy managed to grab hold of her long, thick fur and hold on. Swimming powerfully, Shana towed her to safety at the neighbours' house on higher ground.

It was only half an hour from the time Dorothy and Herman had been sitting, talking with their neighbour, until the time of Dorothy's rescue. But in that short time, they lost everything in their basement. Kevin's and Michele's bedrooms were down there, as well as a laundry room, sewing room and bathroom. The water rose right to the ceiling, and everything in those rooms was either swept away or destroyed — nothing could be salvaged.

Michele was away on holiday — the few clothes she had with her were all she had left of her belongings. Kevin lost everything he owned, as well. Luckily he was working that evening. It was his window that gave way, and if he had been in his room with his door closed, he would have been in trouble when the water cascaded in.

Shana received two awards for her heroism and was the subject of many news stories, including an article in *Dogs in Canada* magazine. Sadly, Shana died of cancer when she was nine years old. She will never be forgotten by Dorothy Laurin, however, nor by her family. Shana was a dog who could overcome her own worst fear in order to save her best friend.

The "Newf"

Descended from Mastiffs brought to Canada by Basque fishermen, the Newfoundland is a massive dog with a thick, double-layered, long black coat that protects it from the cold. They have very strong bones, and webbed paws that make them very much at home in the water. They used to work for fishermen, and would swim out to gather in the nets that their owners spread in the frigid waters off the Newfoundland coast.

Quite often the old sailing ships would have a Newfoundland dog on board to rescue unfortunate sailors who were washed overboard during storms. There are many stories of Newfoundland dogs who have performed heroic rescues. A Newfoundland once swam ashore with a line from a ship that was sinking off the coast of Nova Scotia and helped to haul the passengers and crew to safety. That Newf was awarded a medal from Lloyd's of London, the famous insurance company. Another Newfoundland, so the story goes, once saved the French emperor Napoleon from drowning. Newfoundlands are even used as lifeguards on some beaches in France.

Topnotch with Jim Thomson

TOPNOTCH

The Faithful Friend

Irene Thomson used to do the accounting for the local feedmill near where she lived in Moffat, Ontario. There is some bush near Moffat that's quite wild, and often she would see hunters' cars parked there. One Saturday morning, arriving as usual with her husband, Jim, they saw a terrified little beagle running around. They coaxed it over to them and gave it something to eat.

The next weekend the dog was still there. They fed it again. The little dog began to trust them. They checked the paper for any notices of a lost beagle, but after another week, they decided that the beagle had been dumped on purpose.

Irene wanted to take it home. Jim didn't really want to, but finally he consented. It was a decision that would save his life.

Topnotch was a good, quiet little dog, and very affectionate. He never ran away, the way so many other beagles do. He didn't seem to have any hunting instinct at all, which was probably why he had been abandoned — someone had tried to make a hunter out of him, then abused and dumped him when they were unsuccessful.

Jim started to take the dog on walks with him, and it wasn't long before the small dog became his constant companion.

One morning, Jim and Topnotch left the house around noon. When evening came and they hadn't come home, Irene got worried. Her husband suffers from Parkinson's disease and Alzheimer's, and she was afraid he might have become confused and lost. She called the police, who immediately started a search.

Five days later, Jim Thomson still had not been found. The area is full of trees and swampy ground — and coyotes.

"That's what we were afraid of," Irene says. "Those coyotes howled all night. I thought for sure they got the dog, at least." The searchers started looking for the dog's remains, hoping that would give them some clue as to where Jim might be.

Every morning, when Lynn McBratney came into the Halton Regional Police Station where she works as a station duty clerk, the first thing she asked was whether there was any news yet about Jim Thomson. The answer was always no. "Finally, I just got a real gut feeling that I needed to do something about it," Lynn says. So she asked Sergeant Kim Duncan, who was coordinating the search, if it would be all right if Lynn got a few friends to come out and help. The sergeant was glad to give permission, so Lynn rounded up four friends and the brother of one of them, who was visiting from the Yukon.

They went out bright and early the next morning, and soon were up to their hips in a swamp.

"It was hot — the hottest day of the summer," Lynn says, "and mosquitoes were everywhere."

About noon, Sergeant Duncan took them back to the command post. Many of the other searchers left at that point, but Lynn and her friends were determined to keep on. An auxiliary sergeant, John Tatham, joined them, and the party was taken out to the Shannon Trail. It had been searched a couple of times before, but the rescue parties were getting desperate.

"We were thrashing here and thrashing there," Lynn says. "I was getting far away from the others and couldn't see them, so we were calling to each other to keep in touch. It was really heavy bush in there."

Suddenly one of Lynn's friends called out, "Is that dog tied up?"

"What dog?" Lynn called back.

They all came back to the trail, and Lynn's friend said, "There's a dog barking there." They all stood staring, trying to see if the stand of bush was the back of a farm. It could be a farm dog they were hearing — or it could be Jim Thomson's dog.

"His name is Topnotch," Lynn said. "Let's call him."

So they started calling his name, and were answered by a volley of excited barks.

"Where is that coming from?" Lynn's friend's brother, Ross, asked.

"There." The friend who had first heard the barking pointed.

"Ross hit the bush like a knife," Lynn says, "and about ten seconds later he yelled, 'He's here!'"

"The dog?" Lynn yelled back.

"No. Mr. Thomson!"

Lynn and the others charged into the bush. One stayed out to mark the spot where they had gone in.

Jim Thomson was unconscious and lying in two or three inches of water. He was covered with mosquitoes and other insects. There beside him, refusing to budge, sat Topnotch.

John Tatham, the auxiliary sergeant, radioed for help. Not five minutes later, Sergeant Kim Duncan came running in, unable to believe they'd actually found the missing man. The other members of the search team were quick to arrive, along with members of the emergency response team. They widened the trail so that the ambulance officers could get in, and Mr. Thomson was carried out on a stretcher.

> **"That's what we were afraid of. Those coyotes howled all night. I thought for sure they got the dog, at least."**

A police officer led a worried Topnotch on an improvised leash behind his master. The little dog struggled along the path, but a felled tree in his way finally proved too much for him.

"He just sat down as if to say, 'I've run out of energy,'" Lynn says. "So my friend picked him up and carried him the rest of the way out. When we got back to the command post, we gave him some water and some Timbits."

Topnotch had stayed beside his master for five days and nights. If it hadn't been for his barking, Jim Thomson probably would have died before he was found. The little beagle proved to be a faithful friend indeed, and was one of the inductees into the Ralson Purina Animal Hall of Fame in 1996. He took his place proudly beside the other winners, including Balloo from Alberta, whose story is also written up in this book.

Charlie with Tom Van Impe

CHARLIE

The Dog Who Believed In Returning a Favour

Charlie is a Husky–German Shepherd mix with a thick, soft coat the colour of creamed honey and big, dark brown eyes. He's the kind of dog you look twice at on the street. It wasn't always like this. His owner, Tom Van Impe, found him at an animal shelter in Hamilton when Charlie was about a year and a half old, and he was very different.

"He was the most pathetic, sad little pup you've ever seen," Tom says. "But beautiful, too. You could see he had the potential of becoming a lovely dog."

Tom was probably the only one who could see that. Charlie had been abused, he was sick, his coat was in tatters and ragged and he was as thin as a rail. He was frightened of every sudden movement, of every loud noise. At that point he was a sorry, sickly excuse for a dog.

Their first few months together were difficult. In addition to being frightened of every sudden noise — a car backfiring, even the crackling of a fire — Charlie

157

cringed when Tom so much as picked up a broom. He resisted being cared for and ran away at every opportunity. Tom had to retrieve the dog from the animal shelter four or five times. He began to think he had taken on an impossible task.

Gradually, however, Charlie settled down. Secure in Tom's friendship and care, the dog even began to relax and enjoy life. Tom was able to take him along when he went to work, cutting lawns in the area. Riding in Tom's truck became fun, and Charlie loved it when Tom's customers would come out to pet him.

> **"When I hit the floor, I saw the smoke and realized something was wrong."**

Then, one night, Tom's house caught fire. It was very late autumn, almost early winter. The house was heated with a wood-burning stove; Tom hadn't gotten around to installing a smoke alarm yet. A friend was sleeping on the couch in the living room.

About three in the morning, Tom was awakened by Charlie. The dog had come into the room and was "barking like crazy."

"I thought he had to go out," Tom says, "and I'd already let him out at midnight, so I just said, 'No, it's too early. Come on, Charlie, we're not going out now, go back to sleep.' I rolled over and tried to get back to sleep myself. No way would he let me, though. He grabbed my arm and pulled me right out of bed. He was actually growling at me! When I hit the floor, I saw the smoke and realized something was wrong."

Somehow, a spark from the stove had started a fire. Tom rushed to alert his friend. The two men and Charlie managed to get out of the burning house and call the fire department, but by the time the fire was brought under control, the house had suffered a lot of damage. Firemen at the scene said that Tom and his friend could easily have died from the smoke alone. The dog that Tom had nursed back to health, fed, and made a friend of had repaid him by saving his life.

Tom is married now, and the household has expanded. Charlie accepted Carol and her three sons with immediate affection — but wasn't too sure about Kitty. He and Kitty have since become the best of friends, along with all the other animals. There's another cat, Ti-Cat, and another dog, Rocky. There are even a couple of turtles — big ones. Charlie did sort of gnaw on one once while Tom was cleaning out the tank, but he only chipped a little piece of the shell.

Charlie starts his days off by jostling the bed, rolling over on his back, and demanding a belly rub. A friendly, happy, contented family dog, he's a far cry from the miserable little pup Tom brought home with him all those years ago.

"I really believe that Charlie knew I had saved his life by giving him a good home," Tom says. "He returned the favour by saving mine. He's become my best friend. There's nowhere we don't go together if we can."

Charlie was awarded the Ralston Purina Animal Hall of Fame Award for his act of bravery.

And Tom bought a smoke alarm.

Michael McLuhan MPA

Karleen Bradford has lived all over the world, and now makes her home in Ontario. She is the award-winning author of many books for children, including *The Haunting at Cliff House, The Nine Days Queen, Wrong Again, Robbie* and *There Will Be Wolves* (winner of the 1992 CLA Young Adult Canadian Book Award). She is also the author of *Write Now!*, a guide for young writers. Karleen has taught Creative Writing and Writing for Children for many years and has done workshops and readings in schools and libraries across Canada and overseas.

There have always been pets in the Bradford family, and currently Karleen and her husband Jim share a home with their German Shepherd, Casey.